Playing Math Games

Number Practice for Home and School

by Ann Lewis and Francine Neugebauer

Teaching Resource Center

With special thanks to our students and their families
at High Point, Bay Park, and Frontier Elementary Schools,
and to our supportive friends and colleagues
in the Pinellas County School District.

Published by
Teaching Resource Center
P.O. Box 82777
San Diego, CA 92138

Edited by Anne Linehan and Laura Woodard
Design and production by Janis Poe and Janet Buckwalter
Illustrations by Akemi Aoki

PRINTED IN THE UNITED STATES OF AMERICA
ISBN: 1-56785-019-7

Contents

Introduction

Playing games with children is a great way to have fun with mathematics. By including number games in the curriculum, we capitalize on children's enthusiasm and hard work while providing a natural way for them to drill basic arithmetic facts. When playing games in the classroom on a routine basis, students are actively engaged and getting the repetition needed to be confident in using basic facts while building number sense.

The games do not have to be introduced to your students in the order given. However, the games that are played with each of the materials (dice, cards, and spinners) are generally presented in order of difficulty. Just keep in mind your students' individual needs and skills that might need reinforcement throughout the year.

As an alternative to drill and practice worksheets, these versatile games fit into any classroom setting. They may be used as whole class activities, in small groups, during choice time (in centers), or as students finish an assignment. These options enable the teacher to work with individual students while the others are working with partners, alone, or in small groups. The students are able to work independently because the games are designed to encompass all levels of ability.

Students of different ability levels often work together successfully because they can count the symbols (the symbols on the playing card or the dots on the dice) as needed for support. Some students may use the symbols to work out the problem whereas others may use them to check their work.

Many of the games are similar in design, which allows a child who needs lots of reinforcement to continue practicing the same skill without losing interest. When less able students play card games, it is sometimes helpful to remove higher numbered cards in the beginning and then add them as they become more comfortable playing the games.

These games are easy to implement at school and at home because of the availability of materials and the simplicity of the games. Each game includes a parent newsletter of explanation so the games can be sent home daily, weekly, or as homework assignments. The games are great to share at parent-teacher conferences, open houses, or math nights.

In addition to providing successful drill and practice at home and school, these games also:

- address the NCTM Standards of number sense, problem solving, reasoning, and communication
- motivate students to practice basic facts
- de-emphasize competition to keep the focus on learning
- allow for positive heterogeneous grouping
- provide natural opportunities for performance assessments
- increase children's confidence in their mathematical thinking abilities
- develop number sense in a fun way

Materials

The games use materials that are easy to find and manage. The basic materials include:

- decks of playing cards
- dice
- number cubes
- spinners
- recording paper

Cards

It is helpful to have one deck of cards per child, but it isn't necessary. Most games are played in partners; one deck of cards per two students is sufficient. Remove all of the face cards (kings, queens, jacks and jokers) from each deck. Keep the ace; it will equal one. We have found it easiest to store the decks in separate plastic zip lock sandwich bags. Then we put all the bags together in a basket on the math shelf for easy distribution.

It is helpful and cost effective to have playing cards donated. We have learned through experience that having decks of cards with different pictures makes cleanup and material management much easier. If the decks become mixed up during play, the students can easily sort the cards into the appropriate bags during cleanup.

Blackline masters of basic number-numeral cards are provided to use as an alternative, see pages 68 and 69.

Dice

Most of the dice games are also played in partners, but some dice games are played with two dice, so it's helpful to plan for one die per student. We have found it easiest to store the classroom set of dice together in one zip lock bag.

Number Cubes

Number cubes have numerals or symbols (+,-,<,=) on them. They are easily made by marking on small wooden cubes. Permanent markers work best. To use the same set of cubes throughout the year, use stickers showing the desired numerals and symbols to mark the cubes. As the students' needs change, just change the stickers. A blackline master for operational dice can be found on page 79.

Spinners

Blacklines for basic spinners are included for each game. Blank spinners are also included so the games can be easily adapted to meet the needs of the students as they change over the year. For the blackline spinners, hold the end of a paper clip at the center with a pencil point. Flick the paper clip as you would a spinner. Store bought spinners also work well.

Recording

Once a student becomes confident playing a game, you will want her to record her work. Plain paper works nicely, but you may want to use individual chalk or wipe boards. Some games included in this book have separate blackline masters for recording results. These can be found in the blackline section beginning on page 63.

As students' writing skills advance, we often have them share their discoveries by writing. This writing can be done on plain paper, in journals, on the computer or by using audio or video recordings.

Playing Math Games in the Classroom

Introducing the Games

The games can be introduced in various ways. When all the students will be playing the same game, it can be introduced to the whole group at one time. Gather the students in a circle and demonstrate the game step by step, with a student as your partner. This can also be done using overhead playing cards, spinners, dice and number cubes. Another option is small group demonstrations. These allow the teacher to easily supervise the players and may make the games more manageable in the beginning. If one group of students has learned a game, it can be fun for those students to teach the game to other students.

The first few times the students play may take longer as they are getting used to the materials and the playing rules. Keep the rules simple:

- Use quiet voices.
- Stay in your assigned area.
- Handle the materials with care.
- One player from each group puts the materials away for cleanup.

Once the students have learned the games, there are many appropriate times to play them in your classroom. The times you choose will depend on the needs of your students. These times may include:

- After a whole class lesson
- During choice time (in centers)
- As students finish an assignment

Playing the Games

The games can be played as often as you'd like, depending on the needs of the students. When the whole class is playing at the same time, the teacher facilitates by moving from group to group to observe and talk with the students about their thinking processes. You may also offer variations to particular groups to make the game easier or more challenging. This time is also ideal for doing individual assessments.

Classroom management is a key to implementing the games successfully. Good management allows the students to learn as much as possible from the experience. While the students are playing, take note of the following considerations.

- **Noise level:**
  While it won't be silent when students are working together, sometimes the noise level can be reduced by having the students play in different areas of the classroom.

- **Student movement:**
  Depending on the room arrangement, the students can play at desks or tables, or on the floor around the room.
  Sitting on the floor may be too relaxed for some students. They may need the boundaries of a desk or table top.

Also, observe academic and behavioral issues such as:

- Are the students actively engaged in mathematical thinking?
  If a group is getting off task, try joining the group and playing along with them for a little while to help them get refocused.

- Are the students working cooperatively?
  If not, assign new groups based on behavior or ability levels.

- Does a student appear to be unchallenged?
  Try offering a variation to enrich the game.

During many of the games we have the students record the number sentences that are generated through play. This recording is a natural and necessary extension that bridges the abstract understanding of number to numerals and symbols.

Sharing

Communication is an integral part of the learning process. During sharing, students can talk about the various problem solving strategies they learned while playing. After the first few sessions of playing games, this sharing time provides a natural opportunity to demonstrate team building skills as the students share the mechanics of how they organized with their partners.

After the game, gather the students back together. The sharing session could begin by asking the students, "What did you learn?" Give individuals the opportunity to share if they wish. Often students learn more from listening to a peer than from listening to a teacher.

Another option for beginning the sharing session is for the teacher to share observations about particular students or groups. The observation could be skill-oriented, such as how a particular child worked through a specific problem. Or it could be behavior-oriented, such as how partners settled a dispute or decided who should go first.

Sometimes it is beneficial to have partners reenact a situation that came up while they were playing. Have them share how they figured it out or elicit suggestions from the group of how they could have figured it out. The reenactment can be extended to model further investigation and get students engaged in verbalizing reasoning.

An alternative to sharing with the whole group is having the students write reflections about the experience in journals. Generally, the students write about what they have learned or strategies they used while playing. Some ideas for the students to explore include:

- Write about one thing you learned today while playing the game.
- What is your favorite math game? Why?
- If someone needed practice _____*, what game would you tell them to play? Why?
  (* Name any specific skill.)
- Choose a problem you solved today. Write a different way to solve it.
- What number pattern did you see today?
- Tell a new way to figure out a solution in the game you played today.

Assessing Skills

Once the students are actively engaged in playing, the teacher is free to move about with a clipboard or notebook, jotting down specific anecdotal notes about each student's progress. This is also a time to conference with individuals that need support or enrichment.

When doing a performance assessment, the teacher may ask students to play a specific game and verbalize or record the strategies used. Can the student explain her thinking strategies or reasoning? One way to learn about the student's thinking process is to ask how she arrived at the answer.

Playing Math Games at Home

Playing Math Games is a great way to strengthen the link between school and home. Each game in this book comes with two sets of instructions, one for the classroom and one for the children to take home. Since their enthusiasm will be carried home with them, parents will be encouraged to be a part of this exciting learning experience. Because the materials are so basic, the games can be played almost anywhere and any time the parents have a few spare moments. It is most effective to introduce parents to the games in whole group situations such as Open House or Curriculum Night. At these events, they can learn to play the games with their children while the teacher is present to lend support and answer questions.

The games are designed to work as homework packets or backpacks. Packaging can be as simple as a zip lock bag or as creative as a special backpack, lunch box or suitcase. This will allow for greater efficiency in sending materials home and seeing that they are returned. They also offer a more organized way of communicating with your students' families.

Share with parents the value of playing math games at home and the enjoyment it will bring. The first time you send games home, send a copy of the list of math terms from blackline master page 65 and a copy of the letter to parents from blackline master page 64, or a similar letter you've written. It is important that parents know to not only play the games, but take advantage of the opportunity to talk about math with their children. The games will allow them to have fun while helping their children move from the concrete to the abstract level of mathematics.

Along with the cards, dice or number cubes, include a copy of the parent newsletter provided with each game in this book. You'll also need to attach blacklines for certain games. For games that include blacklines of spinners, make sure that your students understand how to use the spinners well enough to show their family members. (See "Spinners" page 51 or 81 in the blackline section for instructions.) If you are interested, send a copy of the *Rate This Game* response sheet for parents and children to fill out together (found on blackline master page 66). This is a quick and simple way to get feedback on the games and their effectiveness as math drills.

Skill Matrix for Games

A Games	B Early Skills	C Addition	D Subtraction	E Addition/Subtraction	F Place Value
20/20		•			
Addition Shuffle		•			
All Decked Out	•				
Compare	•				
Concentration	•				
Double Compare		•			
Doubles Graph		•			
Flip High,/Flip Low	•				
Go Fish	•				
Graph the Difference			•		
Minus Linus			•		
Money Roll		•			•
Number Cube Difference			•		
Put It In Place					•
Roll and Add		•			
Roll and Subtract			•		
Roll Back One			•		
One Up, One Down		•			
Roll Three		•			
Roll-A-Dollar		•			•
Some Sum		•			
Spin and Spin Again				•	
Spin Up, Spin Down				•	
Subtraction Shuffle			•		
The Whole Deal		•	•	•	
What's The Difference			•		
Write 20, Roll Back			•		
Write 20, Spin Back			•		

Card
Games

All Decked Out

Purpose Practice placing numbers in correct order. Create, analyze, and continue patterns.

Materials one deck of classroom cards

Players one or more

Game

1. Shuffle the cards. Players spread out all of the cards, face up.

2. Each player chooses a card to start with and places it in front of herself, face up.

3. Each player thinks of a pattern she could make that begins with the card she has in front of her. (Examples: 3, 4, 5, 6, and so on; red, black, red, black, and so on; red ace, black 2, red 3, black 4, and so on.) Players take turns choosing cards they can use to continue their patterns.

4. When a player completes a pattern, she replaces her cards face up on the playing surface and starts a different pattern. Play continues until game time is over.

Extension After a pattern is complete, ask the student who made it to "translate" that pattern into another form such as claps and snaps, pattern blocks, or letters. For example, the pattern 9, 9, 8, 8, 7, 7 might translate to I, I, H, H, G, G. Students might also try starting a pattern and challenging a classmate to continue it.

Math News

Skill Update:

Playing *All Decked Out* is an excellent way to introduce your child to math card games! This game gives children counting practice and also helps them connect the words they say when they count ("one, two, three...") with the symbols that stand for numbers.

Try This

Begin with a 10 and work backwards to the ace. Use the ace to stand for 1. Use suits (clubs, diamonds, hearts, and spades) in your patterns, too!

Challenge!

Ask your child to make a pattern that includes all of these at once:
• numbers
• colors (black and red)
• suits (clubs, diamonds, hearts, and spades)

Directions for All Decked Out

Materials   one deck of classroom cards

Players   one or more

Game

1. Shuffle the cards. Spread out all of the cards, face up.

2. Each player chooses a "starter card" and places it in front of him- or herself, face up.

3. Each player thinks of a pattern he or she could make that begins with the starter card. (Examples: 3, 4, 5, 6, and so on; red, black, red, black, and so on; red ace, black 2, red 3, black 4.)

4. If you complete a pattern, put your cards back and start another pattern. Challenge another player to finish a pattern that you started!

Go Fish!

Purpose   Develop one-to-one correspondence skills. Practice identifying numerals.

Materials   one deck of classroom cards

Players   two or more

Game

1. Shuffle the cards. Deal five cards to each player. Players should not let others see their cards. Place the remaining cards face down in a stack in the middle of the players. This stack is the "fish pond."

2. Player A asks the player on her right (Player B) for a certain card that matches one she already has in her hand. If Player B has that card, she must give it to her. Player A places the pair of cards face up in front of her. Then she gets an extra turn.

3. If Player B does not have the card player A asked for, she says, "Go Fish!" This means that Player A must take the top card from the fish pond. If this card matches one in her hand, she places the pair of cards face up in front of her and takes another turn. If it does not match any of her cards, she keeps the card from the fish pond.

4. Players take turns repeating Steps 2 and 3. Play continues until one player runs out of cards or until game time is over. The player with the most matches wins.

Math News

Skill Update:

One-to-one correspondence (matching) is an early math skill that helps children learn to recognize and name numerals.

Just a Note...

The game *Go Fish!* may already be familiar to you. We use *Go Fish!* as a math activity to help children develop number sense through matching. For younger children, part of the challenge may be holding a group of cards in one hand. Show them that hiding your cards from the other players is part of the fun!

Directions for Go Fish!

Materials	one deck of classroom cards
Players	two or more
Game	

1. **Shuffle the cards. Deal five cards to each player. Players should not let others see their cards. Place the remaining cards face down in a stack in the middle of the players. This stack is the "fish pond."**

2. **Player A asks the player on her right (Player B) for a certain card that matches one she already has in her hand. If Player B has that card, he must give it to her. Player A places the pair of cards face up in front of her. Then she gets an extra turn.**

3. **If Player B does not have the card Player A asked for, he says, "Go Fish!" This means that Player A must take the top card from the fish pond. If this card matches one in her hand, she places the pair of cards face up in front of her and takes another turn. If it does not match any of her cards, she keeps the card from the fish pond.**

4. **Players take turns repeating Steps 2 and 3. Play continues until one player makes matches with all of the cards in his or her hand. The player with the most matches wins.**

Family Math

Go Fish! is a great game for the entire family. Go over the directions with your child and then encourage him or her to teach other family members how to play!

Concentration

Purpose   Develop visual memory and practice one-to-one correspondence.

Materials   one deck of cards (include face cards if you wish)

Players   one or more

Game

1. Shuffle the cards. One by one, lay all the cards in the deck face down to form a large rectangle "tiled" with cards.

2. Players take turns flipping two cards face up. The object is to make a match. If the two cards do not match, the player turns them face down again, keeping them in the same positions. If the two cards do match, the player picks them up and places them face down beside her. She then gets another turn.

3. As the game continues, players make more and more matches as they get to know (and remember) the cards' positions.

4. Players continue taking turns until game time is over. The player with the most matches wins.

Talk About It   Ask students to share their strategies for remembering where the cards are.

Math News

Card Game   **Date:**

Skill Update:

Playing *Concentration* is both lots of fun and useful for developing children's visual memory skills. Visual memory skills will help your child do well in many other subject areas besides math, including reading, spelling, art, and science.

Directions for Concentration

Materials   one deck of cards (include face cards if you wish)

Players   one or more

Game

1. Shuffle the cards. One by one, lay all the cards in the deck face down, forming a large rectangle "tiled" with cards.

2. Players take turns flipping two cards face up. The object is to make a match. If the two cards do not match, the player turns them face down again, keeping them in the same positions. If the two cards do match, the player picks them up and places them face down beside him or her. The player then gets another turn.

3. As the game continues, players make more and more matches as they get to know (and remember) the cards' positions.

4. Continue playing until all the cards have been picked up. The player with the most matches wins.

In the Beginning

To make the game easier to play, use half the deck.

Challenge

To make the game more challenging to play, use two decks of cards. Match cards with the same number or suit.

Compare

Purpose   Reinforce number sense by applying the concepts of greater than and less than.

Materials   one deck of classroom cards

Players   two

Game
1. Shuffle the cards. Divide the deck in half. Each player takes a stack, keeping the cards face down.

2. At the same time, players turn over the top cards in their stacks and place them face up on the playing surface. The player with the higher card takes both cards and places them aside in her "keeping pile."

3. If players turn over cards of equal value, there is an "equal compare." Each lays down four cards over the card that matched, three face down, and the fourth face up. The player whose fourth card is higher takes all ten cards and places them in her keeping pile.

4. Play continues until game time is over. If a player runs out of cards, she may use the cards in her keeping pile.

Talk About It   After students have played *Compare*, prompt discussion by asking questions such as these:
- What is the hardest part of this game?
- What is fun about this game?
- How long does it usually take you to figure out whose card is higher?

Extension   To play *Double Compare*, see page 12.

Math News

Date:

Skill Update

We have been learning the terms *greater than* and *less than*. Encourage your child to use these phrases when describing numbers or amounts.

Just a Note...

Playing *Compare* can help your child develop his or her ability to quickly recognize which number in a pair is greater.

Think About It

Encourage your child to explain to you or another family member why we play *Compare* during math time.

Directions for Compare

Materials   one deck of classroom cards

Players   two

Game

1. Shuffle the cards. Divide the deck in half. Each player takes a stack, keeping the cards face down.

2. At the same time, players turn over the top cards in their stacks and place them face up on the playing surface. The player with the higher card takes both cards and places them aside in a "keeping pile."

3. If players turn over cards of equal value, there is an "equal compare." Each lays down four cards, three face down, and the fourth face up. The player whose fourth card is higher gets all ten cards and places them in his or her keeping pile.

4. A player who runs out of cards may use the cards in his or her keeping pile.

5. If you want to, play until a player runs out of cards completely. Then shuffle the cards and play again!

Flip High, Flip Low

Purpose   Develop number sense by exploring the concepts of *greater than* and *less than*.

Note   This game is similar to *Compare*, but is slightly more challenging. You may wish to have students play *Flip High, Flip Low* after they have become experienced *Compare* players.

Materials   one deck of classroom cards

Players   two

Game
1. Shuffle the cards. Divide the deck in half. Each player takes a stack, keeping the cards face down.

2. Player A calls "high" or "low."

3. At the same time, both players flip (turn over and place face up on the playing surface) the top cards in their stacks.

4. If Player A called "high," the player whose card is higher takes both cards for her "keeping pile." If Player A called "low," the player with the lower card takes both cards. If players flip cards of equal value, they place those cards on the bottoms of their stacks.

5. Players repeat Steps 2-4; this time Player B calls "high" or "low."

6. Play continues until game time is over. A player who runs out of cards may continue playing with her keeping pile.

Variation   During each play, players flip two cards instead of one. The player whose cards have the greater or lower sum (depending on the call) takes all four cards.

Math News

Card Game   Date:

Skill Update

In class we are working on building "number sense" by comparing numbers and deciding which one is greater than and which is less than the other.

Just a Note...

Flip High, Flip Low is a fun, fast-moving game that gives children practice with comparing number values.

Challenge

If your child is good at comparing two numbers from 1 to 10 and deciding which is greater, write down or say aloud pairs of two-digit numbers greater than 10. Ask which number is greater than or less than the other.

Directions for Flip High, Flip Low

Materials   one deck of classroom cards

Players   two

Game
1. Shuffle the cards. Divide the deck in half. Each player takes a stack, keeping the cards face down.

2. Player A calls "high" or "low."

3. At the same time, both players flip (turn over and place face up on the playing surface) the top cards in their stacks.

4. If Player A called "high," the player whose card is higher takes both cards for his or her "keeping pile." If Player A called "low," the player with the lower card takes both cards. If players flip cards of equal value, they place those cards on the bottoms of their stacks.

5. Players repeat Steps 2-4; this time Player B calls "high" or "low."

6. Play continues until game time is over. A player who runs out of cards may continue playing with his or her keeping pile.

7. Play as long as you like. The player with the most cards at the end of the game wins.

Double Compare

Purpose

Practice addition facts with sums up to 20 and recognize different combinations of addends with the same sum.

Materials

one deck of classroom cards

Players

two

Game

1. Shuffle the cards. Divide the deck in half. Each player takes a stack, keeping the cards face down.

2. Both players turn over two cards from the top of their stacks and place them face up on the playing surface. The player who turns over the pair with the higher sum takes all four cards and puts them aside in her "keeping pile."

3. If the players turn over pairs of cards with the same sum, there is a "double equal compare." They each turn over five cards, the first three face down, and the final two face up. The player whose final pair has the greater sum takes all 14 cards and puts them in her keeping pile.

4. Play continues until game time is over. If a player runs out of cards, she may use the cards in her keeping pile.

Talk About It

Pose the following scenarios to students after they have played *Double Compare*.
- I turn over a 2 and a 6 and you turn over a 4 and a 4. Do we have an equal compare? Why or why not?
- I turn over a 10 and an ace and you turn over a 6 and a 7. What happens and why?

Math News

Skill Update

Double Compare is a more challenging version of *Compare*. This game gives children practice with addition facts with sums up to 20. Have fun and sharpen your child's addition skills at the same time!

Math at Home

Start an addition notebook. Each time you play *Double Compare*, write down the addition problems that you and your child solve as you play. See how long it takes to fill the book. You might want to give each player his or her very own page in the book!

Directions for Double Compare

Materials   one deck of classroom cards

Players   two

Game

1. Shuffle the cards. Divide the deck in half. Each player takes a stack, keeping the cards face down.

2. Both players turn over two cards from the top of their stacks and place them face up on the playing surface. The player who turns over the pair with the higher sum takes all four cards and puts them aside in a "keeping pile."

3. If the players turn over pairs of cards with the same sum, there is a "double equal compare." They each turn over five cards, the first three face down, and the final two face up. The player whose final pair has the greater sum takes all 14 cards and puts them in his or her keeping pile.

4. Play as long as you want to. If a player runs out of cards, he may use the cards in her keeping pile. The winner is the player who has the most cards at the end of the game.

2 O/2 O

Purpose   Practice adding two or more numbers with sums up to 20.

Materials   one deck of classroom cards
recording paper (optional)

Players   two

Game

1. Shuffle the cards. Remove the top card from the deck and place it face up between the players. This is the "start card" for both players. Divide the remainder of the deck evenly and give each player half. (One player will get an extra card, but it doesn't matter.) Players keep their cards face down in stacks.

2. Player A turns over her top card and places it to the right side of the start card (horizontally). Player A then adds the start card and the card she just put down. If players are recording their work, Player A records her turn with an addition sentence. For example, if the start card is an ace and Player A puts down a 5, she writes $1 + 5 = 6$.

3. Player B repeats Step 2; however, he places his first card below the start card (vertically). He records his work on a separate recording sheet.

4. Players continue to take turns. Player A continues to add to her horizontal line of cards and Player B continues to add to his vertical line. On their recording sheets, the players write a new addition sentence for each turn, writing as addends all of the numbers they have put down so far, as well as the start card's number. For example, if the start card is an ace, on his second turn Player B might write $1 + 3 + 5 = 9$. The goal is to reach 20.

5. Play continues until one player reaches a sum of exactly 20. If a player turns over a card that puts her total over 20, she puts that card on the bottom of her stack and loses a turn.

6. After each game, shuffle the cards and play again. Play until game time is over.

Talk About It   After students have played *20/20*, pose the following scenarios to them:

• Your total is 18. What card or cards do you hope to turn over next?
• Imagine that both players' totals are at 18. All four 2s and all four aces in the deck have already been played. What can you do now?

Extension   Have students use two decks of cards to play *30/30*.

Math News

Directions for 20/20

Materials   one deck of classroom cards
recording paper (optional)

Players   two

Game

1. Shuffle the cards. Remove the top card from the deck and place it face up between the players. This is the "start card" for both players. Divide the remainder of the deck evenly and give each player half. (One player will get an extra card, but it doesn't matter.) Players keep their cards face down in stacks.

2. Player A turns over her top card and places it to the right side of the start card (horizontally). Player A then adds the start card and the card she just put down. If you are recording your work, Player A records her turn with an addition sentence. For example, if the start card is an ace and Player A puts down a 5, she writes 1 + 5 = 6.

3. Player B repeats Step 2; however, he places his first card below the start card (vertically). He records his work on a separate recording sheet.

4. Players continue to take turns. Player A continues to add to her horizontal line of cards and Player B continues to add to his vertical line. On their recording sheets, the players write a new addition sentence for each turn, writing as addends all of the numbers they have put down so far, as well as the start card's number. For example, if the start card is an ace, on his second turn Player B might write 1 + 3 + 5 = 9. The goal is to reach 20.

5. Play continues until one player reaches a sum of exactly 20. If a player turns over a card that puts his or her total over 20, that player puts the card on the bottom of his or her stack and loses a turn.

6. After each game, shuffle the cards and play again. The more rematches you play, the more addition practice your child will get!

Skill Update

Playing *20/20* is lots of fun and is also a great way to practice addition facts with sums up to 20.

Hint

If you run out of low cards (aces, 2s, and 3s) exchange them for higher cards in your stack. For example, find a 4 in your stack and substitute it for two aces and a 2. Then let your opponent reshuffle the remainder of your stack with the aces and 2 to prevent a "stacked deck."

Challenge

Try playing *30/30!* You might want to use two decks of cards.

Subtraction Shuffle

Purpose   Practice subtracting numbers from 1 to 10.

Materials   one deck of classroom cards
recording sheet (optional)

Players   one or more

Game
1. Shuffle the cards and place them in a stack between the players.

2. Player A flips the top two cards and subtracts the lower number from the higher number. If players are recording their work, Player A writes and solves the subtraction sentence.

3. Player B repeats, using a separate recording sheet.

4. Players continue to take turns until game time is over.

Talk About It   Discuss with students how subtraction is like counting backwards. For example, to subtract 5 from 7, you start at 7 and count backwards: 6, 5. You had to say two numbers to get to 5, so 7 - 5 must equal 2.

Math News

Skill Update

Explain to your child that subtraction is like counting backwards. For example, to subtract 5 from 7, you start at 7 and count backwards to 5: 6, 5. You had to count two numbers to get to 5, so 7 - 5 must equal 2! Tell your child that counting back to subtract numbers is the opposite of counting on to add numbers.

Just a Note...

Before playing *Subtraction Shuffle*, make sure your child can easily decide which number in a pair is the larger one. If your child needs more practice with this skill, you might display several pairs of cards and have him or her identify the higher card in each pair. Continue until your child seems very comfortable with this skill. Then play *Subtraction Shuffle* together!

Try This

Help your child use related addition facts to solve subtraction problems. When it is your turn in *Subtraction Shuffle*, demonstrate this for your child by saying your thoughts aloud. For example, if the problem is 7 - 3, you might say, "Let's see, what's the number I'd add to 3 to make 7? It's 4: 3 + 4 = 7. That means that 7 - 3 must equal 4, because addition is the opposite of subtraction."

Just For Fun

Name a number and ask your child to count backwards from that number to zero.

Directions for Subtraction Shuffle

Materials	one deck of classroom cards recording sheet (optional)
Players	one or more
Game	1. Shuffle the cards and place them in a stack between the players.
	2. Player A flips the top two cards and subtracts the lower number from the higher number. If you are recording your work, Player A should write and solve the subtraction sentence.
	3. Player B repeats, using a separate recording sheet.
	4. Continue playing until you run out of cards. Then shuffle the cards and play again!

Addition Shuffle

Purpose   Practice addition facts with sums up to 20.

Materials   one deck of classroom cards
recording paper (optional)

Players   one or more

Game   1. Shuffle the cards and place them face down in a stack.

2. Player A flips the top two cards and adds them. She then sets the cards aside. If players are recording their work, Player A writes and solves the addition sentence.

3. Player B repeats. He records his turns on a separate recording sheet.

4. Players continue to take turns. When the whole stack has been played, shuffle the cards and play again. Continue playing until game time is over.

Note   Monitor groups of students as they play *Addition Shuffle*. If a student gives an incorrect sum, show the same problem on a pair of dice or by sketching sets of objects on the chalkboard. You may wish to have students play with aces through 5s until they have mastered those addition facts and then add the higher cards one by one.

Extension   Challenge students to flip three cards and add them.

Computer Idea   Create a "slide show" of addition problems on a computer hypercard or slide show program. Have students view the problems and answer aloud or in writing.

Math News

Card Game   Date:

Skill Update

Help your child practice "counting on" when adding (it is faster than combining two sets of objects and then counting all of them). When we count on we usually start with the larger number. For example, to solve 7 + 5, start with 7 and count on five times: 8, 9, 10, 11, 12. The sum is 12!

As you play *Addition Shuffle*, demonstrate how to count on by saying your thoughts aloud when it is your turn.

Just a Note...

Playing *Addition Shuffle* gives your child a great opportunity to practice "easy" addition problems such as 1 + 3 = 4. This game also challenges children with more difficult facts such as 7 + 8 = 15. When faced with challenging problems such as these, children are more likely to use the counting-on strategy.

Directions for Addition Shuffle

Materials	one deck of classroom cards recording paper (optional)
Players	one or more
Game	1. Shuffle the cards and place them face down in a stack.
	2. Player A flips the top two cards and adds them, and sets them aside.
	3. Player B repeats.
	4. Players continue to take turns. When the whole stack has been played, shuffle the cards and play again!

Try This

Help your child record the addition problems you each solve as you play *Addition Shuffle*. When you are finished playing, go over your list of addition problems together. Circle the problems that were very easy for your child and put stars by the ones that he or she had to work a little harder to solve!

Challenge

Try flipping three cards and adding them!

Put It in Place

Purpose

Identify values of digits according to their placement in a number.

Materials

one deck of classroom cards (use aces through 9s only)
a place value mat for each player (see blackline master page 71)

Players

two

Game

1. The object of the game is to create a higher two-digit number than your opponent's. Each player uses a place value mat as a playing surface.

2. Shuffle the cards. Divide the deck in half. Each player takes a stack, keeping their cards face down.

3. Each player turns over the top card in her stack and decides whether to place it in the tens place or the ones place on her place value mat. (The idea is to use higher cards in the tens place. 8's and 9's yield two-digit numbers in the eighties and nineties.) Once a card is in place, it cannot be moved!

4. Each player then turns over her second card and places it in the remaining place on her place value mat.

5. The player with the higher two-digit number wins the match. She takes all four cards and puts them in her "keeping pile."

6. Play continues until game time is over. If a player runs out of cards, she may use the cards in her keeping pile.

Extension

Have students play with three cards at a time, creating three-digit numbers. (Use the place value mat on blackline master page 72.)

Challenge

Have students play *Put It in Place* and *Switch:* Use place value mats with three places (see blackline master page 72. Each player draws three cards from her stack and puts them in place according to the rules for *Put It in Place.* After players see their opponents' mats, they are allowed to switch two of their cards only (for instance, they might move the card they had in the hundreds place to the ones place and vice versa). Players also have the option of keeping all of their cards where they are. The winner is determined after both players have made their switches (or not).

Math News

Directions for Put It In Place

Materials   one deck of classroom cards without the 10s
a place value mat for each player

Players   two

Game

1. The object of the game is to create a higher two-digit number than your opponent's. Each player uses a place value mat as a playing surface.

2. Shuffle the cards. Divide the deck in half. Place each half face down in a stack. Each player takes a stack.

3. Each player turns over the top card in his or her stack and decides whether to place it in the tens place or the ones place on the place value mat. Once a card is in place, it cannot be moved!

4. Each player then turns over a second card and places it in the remaining place on the place value mat.

5. The player with the higher two-digit number wins the match. That player takes all four cards and puts them in a "keeping pile."

6. Play continues until game time is over. If a player runs out of cards, he or she may use the cards in the keeping pile.

Skill Update

Playing *Put It In Place* will help your child understand that numerals change their value depending on where they are placed in a two-digit number. For example a 2 can stand for twenty if it is in the tens place or for 2 if it is in the ones place. The idea is to use higher cards in the tens place. (8's and 9's yield two-digit numbers in the eighties and nineties.)

Challenge!

Make your own place value chart and include a column for the hundreds place. Now *Put It in Place* again, this time creating three-digit numbers!

Think About It

Ask your child: After you and I have both placed our first cards, can we always tell who will be the winner? What if one of us puts his or her first card in the ones place? What if we have the same card at the top of our stacks and we each place that card in the tens place?

The Whole Deal

Purpose   Find many ways to get the same sum or difference.

Materials   one deck of classroom cards

Players   one to six

Game

1. Shuffle the cards. Draw one card from the deck. The number shown on the card is known as "the game number."

2. Replace the game number card in the deck and lay all of the cards face up on the playing surface.

3. Players take turns finding pairs of cards that generate numbers equal to the game number through addition or subtraction. For example, if the game number is 7, players might pair 2 and 5 $(2 + 5 = 7)$, ace and 6 $(1 + 6 = 7)$, 10 and 3 $(10 - 3 = 7)$, and so on.

Extension   Instead of having students draw a card to choose the game number, assign them a game number higher than 20 and tell them to find groups of three or more cards with values that add up to the game number.

Math News

Card Game   Date:

Skill Update:

Your child is still a little young for algebra, but he or she is already learning how numbers are related. This important knowledge will provide him or her with a strong foundation for higher-level mathematics!

Just a Note...

It's fun to play *The Whole Deal* with the whole family. The object of this game is to find many ways (through addition and subtraction) to get to the same number!

Challenge!

Instead of drawing a card to choose the game number, think of a game number higher than 20. Then challenge your child to find groups of three or more cards with values that add up to the game number.

Student Corner

Can you think of four more ways to make 6?

$$2 + 4 = 6$$
$$12 - 6 = 6$$
$$ = 6$$
$$ = 6$$
$$ = 6$$
$$ = 6$$

Directions for The Whole Deal

Materials   one deck of classroom cards

Players   one to six

Game
1. Shuffle the cards. Draw one card from the deck. The number shown on that card is known as "the game number."

2. Replace the game number card in the deck and lay all of the cards face up on the playing surface.

3. Players take turns finding pairs of cards that generate numbers equal to the game number through addition or subtraction. For example, if the game number is 7, players might pair 2 and 5 (2 + 5 = 7), ace and 6 (1 + 6 = 7), 10 and 3 (10 - 3 = 7), and so on.

4. Play until all possible combinations have been found. Choose a new number and play again!

Dice Games

Roll and Add

Purpose   Practice addition facts with sums up to 12.

Materials   two dice
recording paper (optional)

Players   one or more

Game
1. Player A rolls two dice and adds the numbers. If players are recording their work, Player A should write the addition sentence shown on the dice, including the answer. (For instance, if a player rolls a 2 and a 4, she should write 2 + 4 = 6.)

2. Player B repeats.

3. Players continue taking turns until game time is over.

Talk About It   After students have played *Roll and Add*, prompt discussion by asking questions:
- What is the highest sum you could possibly get in this game? Why?
- What is the lowest sum you could possibly get? Why?

Math News

Dice Game   **Date:**

Skill Update:

Help your child practice a quick way to add: "counting on" from the larger number in an addition problem. For example, to find the sum of 4 and 3, start with 4 and then count on three times: 5, 6, 7. The answer is 7. You may need to remind your child to begin counting on after the first number in the problem. (To solve the problem above we started counting on with 5, not with 4.) As you play *Roll and Add*, demonstrate how to count on correctly when it is your turn.

Directions for Roll and Add

Materials   two dice
                 recording paper (optional)

Players   one or more

Game   1. **Player A rolls two dice and adds the numbers shown. If you have decided to record your work, Player A should write the addition sentence shown on the dice, including the answer. (For example, if a player rolls a 2 and a 4, he or she should write 2 + 4 = 6.)**

                 2. **Player B repeats.**

                 3. **Have fun playing for 5 to 10 minutes or more!**

Just a Note...

Playing *Roll and Add* is a great way to practice solving addition problems with sums up to 12!

Moving Ahead in Math

Sometimes your child may count dots on the dice to find a sum. Your child may do this even though he or she has already learned, for example, that 2 dots and 4 dots add up to 6 dots. Watch carefully to see whether your child is counting dots out of habit or because he or she really needs to do so to find a sum. If counting dots appears to be a habit, show how you would solve the problem by saying your thoughts aloud.

Roll and Subtract

Purpose   Practice subtracting with numbers from 1 to 6.

Materials   two dice
                       recording paper (optional)

Players   one or more

Game   1. Player A rolls two dice and subtracts the smaller number from
                          the larger number. If players are recording their work, Player A
                          writes the subtraction sentence she has just solved, including
                          the answer.

                       2. Player B repeats.

                       3. Players continue to take turns until game time is over.

Extension   Challenge your students by having them play *Roll and
                       Subtract* with number cubes numbered 1-6 and 7-12, or
                       other number combinations.

Math News

Date:

Skill Update

Your child may describe subtraction by saying, "You take away the smaller number from the bigger number." Help your child understand that subtraction is the difference between two numbers. Show him or her that you can find a difference either by counting up or by counting back.

For example, to solve the problem 7 minus 4, you can start with 4 and count up to 7: 5, 6, 7; or you can start with 7 and count back to 4: 6, 5, 4. Either way, you counted three numbers, so the difference is 3!

Directions for Roll and Subtract

Materials   two dice
recording paper

Players   one or more

Game
1. Player A rolls two dice and subtracts the smaller number from the larger number shown. Player A then writes the subtraction problem he or she has just solved, including the answer.

2. Player B repeats.

3. Continue playing until each player has solved ten subtraction problems and recorded each one. Have fun!

Before You Play

Before playing *Roll and Subtract*, make sure your child can compare the numbers shown on two dice and decide which number is larger than the other. If he or she cannot do so easily, practice this skill with your child until he or she has mastered it.

Moving Ahead in Math

Does your child always count back from the larger number when subtracting? If so, remind him or her to try counting up from the smaller number to the larger number (see *Skill Update* above). Model this skill for your child by saying your thoughts aloud when it is your turn to play: "I rolled a 6 and a 2. This time I think I'll start with 2 and count up to 6: 3, 4, 5, 6. I counted 4 numbers, so the difference must be 4!"

For Fun

Find a cube shaped box. Work with your child to wrap the box in plain paper and write numerals or dots on each of the six sides. Now you've got your own giant die!

Number Cube Difference

Purpose   Practice subtraction with numbers from 1 to 12.

Materials   two number cubes, one numbered 1-6 and one numbered 7-12
                 recording paper

Players   one or more

Game
1. Player A rolls both number cubes and subtracts the smaller number from the larger number. She then writes the number sentence she just solved, including the answer.

2. Player B repeats.

3. Players continue to take turns until game time is over.

Talk About It   After students have played *Number Cube Difference*, prompt discussion by asking questions:
- What differences did you get most often as you played? Why do you think this happened?
- How does knowing that 7 + 5 = 12 help you figure out the difference between 12 and 7?

Math News

Dice Game   **Date:**

Skill Update

We adults take numerals (1, 2, 3, and so on) for granted, but young children need lots of counting practice with real objects and pictures of real objects before they are able to connect this squiggly shape "3" with three baseballs or three cats. In this game we are moving away from pictures that stand for numbers. Your child is making an important step: he or she is now ready to use numerical symbols.

Directions for Number Cube Difference

Materials   two number cubes, one numbered 1-6, and one numbered 7-12
                recording paper

Players   one or more

Game   1. Player A rolls both number cubes and subtracts the smaller number from the larger number. The player then writes a number sentence to record the problem he or she just solved, including the answer.

                2. Player B repeats.

                3. Try to play until you have rolled all possible number combinations. If a player rolls a combination that has already been rolled and recorded, he or she loses a turn!

Just a Note...

The purpose of this game is to practice subtracting from numbers up to 12.

Don't Forget to Record Your Work!

When your child writes subtraction facts such as 12 - 5 = 7, he or she is building an understanding of the subtraction process. Recording math sentences also helps your child make the important connection between spoken language and the symbols used to represent it, as well as the connection between real-world objects and math symbols.

Talk About It!

Ask your child to tell you about addition and subtraction. How are they related to each other? Help your child express this concept by asking questions such as: "You know that 6 + 6 = 12. How does this help you figure out what 12 - 6 equals?"

Graph the Difference

Purpose

Practice subtraction with numbers from 1 to 12. Graph the differences and make observations about the graph.

Materials

two number cubes, one numbered 1-6 and one numbered 7-12
Graph the Difference graph (see blackline master page 74)

Players

one or more

Game

1. Player A rolls both number cubes and subtracts the smaller number from the larger number shown. On the graph, she colors a square that is above the answer.

2. Player B repeats.

3. Players continue taking turns until each player has rolled at least ten times.

4. Players talk about the results they recorded on their graph.

Talk About It

After students have played *Graph the Difference*, prompt discussion by asking questions:
- What difference did you roll most often? Why do you think this difference was rolled more often than any other?
- What difference did you roll least often? Why do you think this difference wasn't rolled more times?
- How many subtraction facts can you think of with a difference of 6?
- Are any squares colored in above the number 12? Why would this be impossible with the number cubes we were using?

Math News

Dice Game   **Date:**

Skill Update

Recording results on a graph is a great way to find math patterns. You can use graphs to help your child predict results and check whether those predictions come true. This will help get your child ready for the branch of math called "probability."

Just a Note...

This game provides practice subtracting from numbers up to 12. It also provides graphing practice.

Talk About It

Use questions like these to prompt your child to discuss the graph you created as you played *Graph the Difference*:

- What difference did you roll most often? Why do you think this difference was rolled more often than any other?
- What difference did you roll least often? Why do you think this difference wasn't rolled more times?
- Is there more than one way to roll a difference of 5?
- How many subtraction facts can you think of with a difference of 6?
- Are any squares colored in above the number 12? Why would this be impossible with the number cubes we were using?
- Do you think the graph would look the same if we played again? Explain why you think so.

Directions for Graph the Difference

Materials   two number cubes, one numbered 1-6 and one numbered 7-12
Graph the Difference graph (attached to this newsletter)

Players   one or more

Game
1. Player A rolls both number cubes and subtracts the smaller number from the larger number. He or she then colors a square on the graph that is above the answer.

2. Player B repeats.

3. Continue playing until each player has rolled at least ten times.

4. Talk about the results you recorded on your graph.

Doubles Graph

Purpose Practice the addition strategy of doubling numbers. Graph the results.

Materials one die
Doubles Graph graph (see blackline master page 75)

Players one or more

Game
1. Player A rolls the die. She then doubles the number shown and colors a square on the graph above the sum.

2. Player B repeats.

3. Play continues until each player has rolled ten times.

4. Players talk about their graph, identifying patterns and making generalizations.

5. Players predict what would happen if they rolled the die ten more times. They then check to see if their prediction comes true.

Talk About It After students have played *Doubles Graph*, prompt discussion by asking questions:
- What patterns do you see on your graph?
- Why do some numbers on the graph have no colored-in squares above them?
- What is the same about all of the numbers that do have colored-in squares above them?

Extension Have your students play *Doubles Plus One*: Roll one die, double the number shown, add 1, and graph that sum. Repeat at least ten times. After they play, ask students how the *Doubles Plus One* graph compares to the *Doubles Graph*.

Math News

Date:

Skill Update

Doubles such as 2 + 2 = 4 and 8 + 8 = 16 are often the first mathematical facts that children learn. Knowing doubles can make it easier to learn other addition facts. For example, if you know that 6 + 6 = 12, it is easy to figure out that 6 + 5 = 11 and that 6 + 7 = 13.

Just a Note...

In this game your child will practice doubling numbers and graphing the results.

Talk About It!

Take time to discuss the graph you have created. Prompt your child by asking questions like, "What is the same about all of the numbers with colored-in squares above them? "

One Step Further

Each player rolls ten more times. Before you begin, ask your child to predict how the graph will change.

Directions for Doubles Graph

Materials	one die *Doubles Graph* graph (attached to this newsletter)
Players	one or more
Game	1. **Player A rolls the die. Then he or she doubles the number shown and colors a square on the graph above the sum.** 2. **Player B repeats.** 3. **Play continues until each player has rolled ten times.**

One Up, One Down

Purpose   Practice adding and subtracting 1.

Materials   a number cube numbered 7-12
                a cube with plus and minus symbols on it (or see blackline
                    master page 79)
                recording paper

Players   one or more

Game   1. Player A rolls both cubes and records the number and
                   the symbol shown, followed by a numeral 1. She then
                   solves the addition or subtraction problem. For
                   example, if she rolls a 7 on one cube and a plus sign on
                   the other, she writes 7 + 1 = 8.

                2. Player B repeats.

                3. Players continue taking turns until game time is over.

Talk About It   Use the chalkboard or an overhead projector to record
                    some of the number sentences students generated as they played
                    One Up, One Down. Ask how an odd or even number changes
                    when 1 is added to or subtracted from it. Encourage your
                    students to make generalizations such as, "If a number is odd and
                    you add 1 to it, the sum is always even."

Extension   Change the numerals on the cube to higher numerals.
                Then have students play *One Up, One Down* again.

Math News

Dice Game   **Date:**

Skill Update

Once your child knows how to add and subtract 1 from other numbers, he or she can have fun applying this strategy to large numbers. For example, what does 100 + 1 equal? What about 100 - 1? How about 1,000 + 1 and 1,000 - 1?

Challenge

Name some large numbers and ask your child to add or subtract 1 from each of them.

Talk About It

Ask your child, "How is playing this game like counting?"

Directions for One Up, One Down

Materials	a number cube numbered 7-12 a cube with plus and minus symbols on it recording paper
Players	one or more
Game	1. Player A rolls both cubes and records the number and the symbol shown, followed by a numeral 1. He or she then solves the addition or subtraction problem. For example, if Player A rolls a 7 on one cube and a plus sign on the other, he or she writes 7 + 1 = 8.
	2. Player B repeats.
	3. Continue playing for about ten minutes.

Student Corner

Can you do this?

$$100 - 1 =$$
$$100 + 1 =$$

Or this?

$$56 + 1 =$$
$$56 - 1 =$$

Or this?

$$34 + 1 =$$
$$34 - 1 =$$

Roll-a-Dollar

Purpose   Practice adding dimes and pennies to make one dollar.

Materials   dime and penny die (see blackline master page 76)
dimes and pennies (play money or real coins)

Players   one or more

Game

1. Collect the coins in a "bank." You might use two bowls or saucers, one for dimes and one for pennies. Player A rolls the dime and penny die and takes the coin shown from the bank.

2. Player B repeats.

3. Player A rolls again, takes the coin shown from the bank, and tells how many total cents she has now.

4. Players continue to take turns. When a player has collected 10 pennies, she should exchange them for a dime. Play continues until a player has exactly one dollar. If a player rolls an amount that will put her total over a dollar, she does not take that coin. Instead, she loses a turn.

Talk About It

After students play *Roll-a-Dollar*, prompt discussion by asking questions:

- What coins can you trade 11 pennies for?
- What coins can you trade 25 pennies for?
- If you have 96 cents and you roll a dime, what happens?
- In this game, what is the only way to get to a dollar if you have 96 cents?

Math News

Dice Game

Date:

Skill Update

We are practicing counting dimes and pennies. We start with dimes and pennies so your child can practice counting by tens and ones. Before playing *Roll-a-Dollar*, ask your child to count aloud by tens to 100 and by ones to 10.

Think About It

Ask your child, "If you rolled ONLY dimes, how many turns would it take you to get a dollar?"

Challenge

Ask, "If you had a die with only quarters on it, how many rolls would it take you to get a dollar?"

Math at Home

Buy or make a piggy bank (or kitty bank or rhino bank!) for saving coins. Help your child count the coins each week. You might help your child practice subtraction skills by letting him or her "withdraw" a certain amount each week to buy a treat or toy.

Directions for Roll-a-Dollar

Materials	dime and penny die dimes and pennies (play money or real coins)
Players	one or more
Game	1. Collect the coins in a "bank." You might use two saucers, one for pennies and one for dimes. Player A rolls the dime and penny die and takes the coin shown from the bank.
	2. Player B repeats.
	3. Player A rolls again, takes the coin shown from the bank, and tells how many total cents he or she has now.
	4. Players continue to take turns. When a player has collected 10 pennies, he or she should exchange it for a dime. Play continues until one player has exactly one dollar. If a player rolls a coin that will put his or her total over a dollar, he or she does not take that coin; instead, the player loses a turn.

Money Roll

Purpose
Practice adding coins to make one dollar.

Materials
coin die (see blackline master page 77)
pennies, nickels, dimes, and quarters (play money or real coins)
hundreds chart (blackline master page 78) optional

Players
one or more

Game

1. Collect the coins in a "bank." You might want to use a separate bowl or saucer for each type of coin. Player A rolls the die and takes the coin shown from the bank.

2. Player B repeats.

3. Player A rolls again, takes the coin shown, and tells how many total cents she has now.

4. Players continue to take turns. They should exchange coins of lesser value for those of higher value whenever they have the combinations of coins needed to do so. Play continues until a player's coins add up to exactly one dollar. If a player rolls a coin that will bring her total over a dollar, she does not take that coin. Instead, she loses a turn.

Talk About It
Display a hundreds chart or provide students with a copy of blackline master 78. Ask questions such as:
- Where would you place dimes on this chart?
- Where would you place nickels?
- Where would you place pennies?
- How about quarters?
- Where would you place a one dollar bill on the chart?
- How many charts would you use to show ten dollars?

Math News

Skill Update

Help your child develop "number sense" by relating numbers to coin values. For example, ask what coins your child would use to show the number 17. Then ask what number your child would write to stand for a quarter.

Just a Note...

Playing this game gives your child an opportunity to practice counting coins to sums of one dollar.

Try This

Make a chart like the one below to keep track of your coins. You can make your chart big enough to stack your coins in the correct columns or you can write tally marks (卌) in the columns to show how many you have of each type of coin. Be sure to use pencils so you can erase your tally marks when you exchange coins.

25¢	10¢	5¢	1¢

Directions for Money Roll

Materials　　coin die
pennies, nickels, dimes, and quarters
(play money or real coins)

Players　　one or more

Game

1. Collect the coins in a "bank." You might want to use a separate bowl or saucer for each type of coin. Player A rolls the die and takes the coin shown from the bank.

2. Player B repeats.

3. Player A rolls again, takes the coin shown, and tells how many total cents he or she has now.

4. Players continue to take turns. They should exchange coins of lesser value for those of higher value whenever they have the combinations of coins needed to do so. Play continues until a player's coins add up to exactly one dollar. If a player rolls a coin that will bring his or her total over a dollar, he or she does not take that coin. Instead, the player loses a turn.

Student Corner

How much money is this?

two quarters
plus
two dimes
plus
three nickels
plus
five pennies

Use real coins or play money to help you count.

Roll Three

Purpose

Practice adding three numbers.

Materials

one die
recording paper

Players

one or more

Game

1. Player A rolls the die three times. She records the three numbers, adds them, and records their sum, writing a number sentence. For example:
   1 + 6 + 4 = 11.

2. Player B repeats, using his own sheet of recording paper.

3. Players continue taking turns until game time is over.

Extension

Challenge students by having them play *Roll Four, Roll Five,* or *Roll Six.* You might give them long, narrow strips of paper or some adding machine tape for recording their work.

Math News

Dice Game   **Date:**

Skill Update

When we add three numbers we can use grouping strategies. For example, to add 5 + 3 + 5, we can quickly add 5 + 5, and then add 3 more for a sum of 13.

Think About It

Ask your child, "If you are playing *Roll Three* with a die numbered 1, 2, 3, 4, 5, and 6, what is the highest sum you can roll? What is the lowest sum you can roll?

Challenge

If your child has successfully played *Roll Three* many times and is still eager to play, try playing *Roll Four* or *Roll Five!*

Math At Home

Work with your child to invent your own game that involves adding three numbers. Encourage your child to share the game you invented with the class.

Directions for Roll Three

Materials   one die
               recording paper

Players   one or more

Game
1. **Player A rolls the die three times. He or she records the three numbers, adds them, and records their sum, writing a number sentence. For example: 1 + 6 + 4 = 11.**

2. **Player B repeats, using his or her own sheet of recording paper.**

3. **Continue playing for about ten minutes.**

Student Corner

Solve:
6 + 3 + 6 + 3 =
5 + 2 + 5 + 2 =

Tell how you grouped the numbers to solve the problems quickly. Write two more problems like these two and give them to a family member to solve.

Write 20, Roll Back

Purpose   Practice subtracting with numbers from 1 to 20.

Materials   one die
recording paper

Players   one or more

Game

1. Player A writes the numeral 20 on her recording sheet. She then rolls the die and subtracts the number shown from 20, writing a number sentence. For example, if she rolls a 6, she writes 20 - 6 = 14.

2. Player B repeats.

3. Player A rolls the die again and subtracts the number shown from the difference she got when she completed Step 1. For example, if her first number sentence is 20 - 6 = 14, and she rolls a 5 on her second turn, she writes 14 - 5 = 9.

4. Player B repeats.

5. Players continue to takes turns rolling the die and subtracting the number shown from the difference they got on their last turn. The game ends when one player gets a difference of 5 or less.

Talk About It

After students have played *Write 20, Roll Back*, prompt discussion by asking questions:
- What did you learn from this game?
- What is the lowest number of turns it could take a player to reach a difference of 5 or less?
- What is the greatest number of turns it could take a player to reach a difference of 5 or less?

Extension

Have your students play *Write 30, Roll Back*. They may want to try using a number cube numbered 7-12 instead of a die.

Math News

Skill Update

This game is a lot of fun! It's also great for practicing subtraction with two-digit numbers.

Talk About It

Ask your child:
- How many times did you have to roll to get to 5 or less?
- Could you have reached 5 or less in fewer rolls?
- If you have 10, what numbers do you hope to roll on your next turn? Why?

Challenge

Try playing *Write 30, Roll Back*. You might want to use a number cube numbered 7-12 instead of a die.

Directions for Write 20, Roll Back

Materials   one die
                  recording paper

Players   one or more

Game   1. **Player A writes the numeral 20 on his or her recording sheet, rolls the die, and subtracts the number shown from 20, writing a number sentence. For example, if Player A rolls a 6, he or she writes 20 - 6 = 14.**

2. **Player B repeats.**

3. **Player A rolls the die again and subtracts the number shown from the difference he or she got when completing Step 1. For example, if Player A's first number sentence is 20 - 6 = 14, and he or she rolls a 5 on the second turn, he or she writes 14 - 5 = 9.**

4. **Player B repeats.**

5. **Players continue to take turns rolling the die and subtracting the number shown from the difference they got on their last turn, writing a new number sentence each time. The game ends when one player gets a difference of 5 or less.**

Roll Back One

Purpose   Help students understand the relationship between subtraction and counting back.

Materials   one die
                   recording paper

Players   one or more

Game   1. Player A rolls the die, records the number, and subtracts 1 from it, writing a number sentence. For example, if she rolls a 3, she writes 3 - 1 = 2.

                   2. Player B repeats.

                   3. Players continue to take turns until game time is over.

Extension   When students are competent at subtracting 1 from numbers up to 6, encourage them to use two or more dice. This will give students addition practice, as well.

Math News

Skill Update

When your child subtracts 1 from other numbers, he or she is using the counting back strategy. When playing games like *Roll Back One*, children use what they already know about counting back to help them subtract.

Just a Note...

Playing *Roll Back One* gives your child practice with writing subtraction sentences and helps him or her make the connection between subtraction and counting back.

Challenge

Play the following variation of *Roll Back One*: Roll two or more dice. Then subtract 1 from the sum of the numbers shown on both or all of the dice.

Special Request to Family Members

Let me know what you think about this game. Did your family try the challenge activity? Was your child interested in playing more than once?

Directions for Roll Back One

Materials	one die recording paper
Players	one or more
Game	1. Player One rolls the die, records the number shown, and subtracts 1 from it, writing a number sentence. For example, if Player A rolls a 3, he or she writes 3 - 1 = 2.
	2. Player B repeats.
	3. Continue playing until each player has recorded ten number sentences. Play again if you'd like!

Some Sum

Purpose   Practice identifying addition facts that have the same sum.

Materials   one die
                     recording paper
                     clock or timer (optional)

Players   one or more

Game   1. Players work together. They roll the die and write the number
                        rolled at the top of their recording sheet.

                     2. Players think of and record as many addition facts as they can
                        with the sum at the top of their recording sheet. (Remind
                        students to include addition facts with 0 in them!)

                     3. Players roll again to get a different sum. Using another sheet of
                        recording paper, they repeat Steps 1 and 2.

Note   Give students a time limit for completing Step 2. (However, keep
                     in mind that some students do not do their best math work
                     when under time pressure.) Some students may enjoy taking
                     turns acting as timekeeper.

Math News

Skill Update

Thinking of many combinations of numbers that add up to a given sum helps children understand how numbers are related to one another.

Just a Note...

This game will give your child an opportunity to identify addition facts that have the same sum. For example, $1 + 5 = 6, 0 + 6 = 6, 1 + 2 + 3 = 6$, and so on.

Here's Another Idea

Play *Some Difference*: Roll the die and think of as many subtraction problems as you can with that number as the answer. Warning: The possibilities are infinite. For example, if you roll a 6, you might write:

$1006 - 1000 = 6$
$10,006 - 10,000 = 6$
$100,006 - 100,000 = 6$
$1,000,006 - 1,000,000 = 6$

and so on and so on and so on...

Directions for Some Sum

Materials   one die
recording paper
timer or clock (optional)

Players   one or more

Game

1. Work with your child. Have him or her roll the die and write the number rolled at the top of your recording sheet.

2. Together, think of and write down as many addition facts as you can that have the sum you wrote at the top of your sheet. Remember to include addition facts with zero in them! If you want to, give yourselves a time limit (such as one minute or five minutes) to write all of the number sentences you can think of.

3. Roll the die again to get a different sum. Using another sheet of paper, repeat Steps 1 and 2.

4. At the end of the game, count to see how many number sentences you wrote for each sum. Make sure all of your addition facts are correct!

Student Corner

Can You Do This?

10

$1 + 9 = 10$
$2 + 8 = 10$
$3 + 7 = 10$
$4 + 6 = 10$

What comes next?

_____ + _____ = _____

What patterns do you see?

Spinner Games

Quick and easy spinner assembly:

Hold the end of a paper clip at the center with a pencil point.
Flick the paper clip as you would for a spinner.

What's the Difference?

Purpose   Practice subtracting from numbers up to 9.

Materials   *What's the Difference?* spinners (see blackline master page 82)
recording paper
paper clip

Players   one or more

Game   1. Player A chooses one of the *What's the Difference?* spinners.

2. Player A spins the spinner. She subtracts the number it lands on from the number in the center of the spinner, writing a subtraction sentence to record her turn.

3. Player B repeats Step 2.

4. Players continue taking turns. If a player spins a number sentence she has already recorded, she loses a turn.

5. The first player to spin all eight possible subtraction problems gets to choose the next spinner.

Note   This simple game offers a good opportunity for players to learn how to construct and spin the spinner using a pencil and paper clip.

Extension   Customize a spinner that meets your students' needs using the blank *What's the Difference?* spinner on blackline master page 83.

Math News

Spinner Game

Date:

Skill Update

We have been subtracting from numbers up to 9 and recording our work by writing subtraction sentences. Playing *What's the Difference?* is a great way to practice these skills!

Just a Note...

What's the Difference? provides practice in subtracting other numbers from 7, 8, and 9.

Talk About It

Ask your child, "When do we use subtraction at home? How do we usually figure out the answers to subtraction problems we solve at home? Do we usually write out the problem on paper or figure it out in our heads using 'mental math'?"

Taking It Further

Work with your child to think of a new game that involves subtraction. Encourage your child to share your new game with the class!

Student Corner

Draw your own spinner for playing *What's the Difference?* Make the game harder to play by changing the numbers.

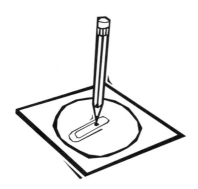

Directions for What's the Difference?

Materials
: *What's the Difference?* spinners (attached to this newsletter)
recording paper
a paper clip

Players
: one or more

Game
: 1. Player A chooses one of the *What's the Difference?* spinners.

  2. Player A spins the spinner. He or she subtracts the number it lands on from the number in the center of the spinner, writing a subtraction sentence to record the turn.

  3. Player B repeats Step 2.

  4. Players continue taking turns. If a player spins a number sentence he or she has already recorded, that player loses a turn.

  5. The first player to spin all eight possible subtraction problems gets to choose the next spinner.

  6. Play again!

Spin and Spin Again

Purpose

Practice adding various numbers and recording addition sentences. Practice using the commutative property.

Materials

Spin and Spin Again spinner (see blackline master page 84)
paper clip
recording paper

Players

one or more

Game

1. Player A spins twice and records the two numbers spun in an addition sentence. Then she uses the commutative property to write a second number sentence. For example, if she spins a 3 and a 9, she writes 3 + 9 = 12 and 9 + 3 = 12.

2. Player B repeats.

3. Players continue taking turns, checking to be sure that they and their opponents solve their addition problems correctly. If a player spins an addition problem that she has already recorded, she lose a turn.

4. Play continues until game time is over.

Note

The commutative property: The order in which the numbers are added does not change the sum.

Math News

Skill Update

Here is an example of the commutative property of addition: 2 + 3 = 3 + 2. This property says that no matter what order in which you add two or more numbers, they add up to the same sum.

Directions for Spin and Spin Again

Materials
- spinner (attached to this newsletter)
- recording paper
- paper clip

Players
- one or more

Game

1. **Player A spins twice and records the two numbers spun in an addition sentence. Then he or she uses the commutative property to write a second number sentence. For example, if Player A spins a 3 and a 9, he or she writes 3 + 9 = 12 and 9 + 3 = 12.**

2. **Player B repeats.**

3. **Players continue taking turns. Check to be sure all of the players solve their addition problems correctly. If a player spins an addition problem that he or she has already recorded, that player loses a turn.**

4. **The first player to write ten correct number sentences wins!**

Just a Note...

Playing *Spin and Spin Again* is a great way to become familiar with the commutative property.

Challenge

Help your child make a new spinner with higher numbers on it. Then play again!

Talk About It

Name an addition sentence and ask your child to tell you its "commutative partner," or another order in which to state the problem.

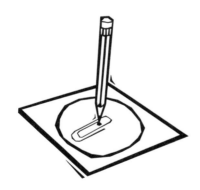

Write 20, Spin Back

Purpose

Practice subtracting various numbers from 20. Practice recording subtraction sentences.

Materials

Write 20, Spin Back spinner (see blackline master page 86)
recording paper
paper clip

Players

one or more

Game

1. Player A spins and subtracts the number she spun from 20. She writes a subtraction sentence to record her turn.

2. Player B repeats.

3. Play continues until one player has recorded all ten possible subtraction sentences. If a player spins a number she has already spun, she loses a turn.

Extension

Have students play another version of *Write 20, Spin Back*: On each player's second turn, she writes the difference she got for Step 1, spins, and subtracts the number spun from that difference, writing a new number sentence. Players continue to take turns. If a player reaches zero, she should start again at 20. If she spins a number greater than the difference from her last turn, she spins again.

Math News

Spinner Game   Date:

Skill Update

If your child has difficulty subtracting other numbers from 20, give him or her some items to use as counters. You might use dried peas, paper clips, pennies, pebbles, or small toys.

Take It Further

Play another version of *Write 20, Spin Back*: On each player's second turn, he or she writes the difference from Step 1, spins, and subtracts the number spun from that difference, writing a new number sentence. Players continue to take turns. If a player reaches zero, he or she should start again at 20. If a player spins a number greater than the difference from the last turn, he or she spins again.

Challenge

Try playing *Write 30, Spin Back*!

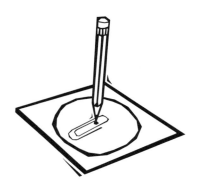

Direction for Write 20, Spin Back

Materials   spinner (attached to this newsletter)
recording paper
paper clip

Players   one or more

Game
1. Ask your child to show the other players how to make a spinner with a pencil and a paper clip.

2. Player A spins and subtracts the number spun from 20. He or she writes a subtraction sentence to record the turn.

3. Player B repeats.

4. Play continues until one player has recorded all ten possible subtraction sentences. If a player spins a number he or she has already spun, that player loses a turn.

Minus Linus

Purpose

Practice subtraction using a number line. Practice recording subtraction sentences.

Materials

Minus Linus number line (see blackline master page 88)
Minus Linus spinner (see blackline master page 89)
recording paper
paper clip
a *Minus Linus* pointer for each player (this might be a pencil or an arrow cut from colored construction paper or the blackline master on page 91)

Players

one or more

Game

1. Cut out and construct the number line by gluing or taping the two halves together.

2. Each player places her pointer above 20 on the number line and writes 20 on her recording sheet.

3. Player A spins the spinner. To find the difference between 20 and the number she spun, she moves her pointer that number of marks down the number line. Her pointer should now be pointing to the difference; she keeps it pointing to that number until her next turn. Player A then records her turn by writing a subtraction sentence.

4. Player B repeats Step 2.

5. When Player A takes her second turn, she spins the spinner and uses her pointer to subtract the number she spun from the difference she got for her first turn.

6. Players continue to take turns spinning, using their pointers to subtract, and recording their turns with subtraction sentences. If a player spins a number greater than her last difference, she spins again. The first player to reach an exact difference of 1 wins.

Math News

Skill Update

In class we are exploring the idea that subtraction is like moving down (instead of up) a number line. This helps us figure out that the answer to a subtraction problem is always less than the number we started with!

Just a Note...

Minus Linus uses a cute lion character and a spinner to help children move down the number line when they subtract.

Challenge

Ask your child to make a number line that goes up to 30, 40, or even 50! Then play Super Minus Linus.

Math at Home

Work with your child to invent a new math game that includes Linus. Encourage your child to share your new game with the class!

Try This

Help your child make a kind of number line called a timeline. Begin at about 1930 and end with 2010. Start Linus on the mark for the current year. Count back each of your ages to find the years when you were born! Encourage your child to bring your timeline to class.

Directions for Minus Linus

Materials
number line
spinner
Minus Linus pointer

Game
Linus sits on the number line at 20. Spin the spinner to get a number to subtract from 20. Use Linus to count down that many spaces on the number line. See what number he lands on. Keep spinning and subtracting from whatever number Linus was on last until you reach 1. If you spin a number that is higher than the number Linus is on, you must move him back to 20! You and your child can play together, or you can use separate Linuses (copy his picture) and take turns spinning. The first player to get to 1 without going any lower wins.

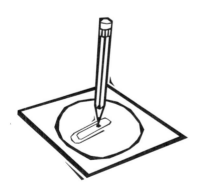

Spin Up, Spin Down

Purpose

Practice adding two numbers. Practice adding or subtracting 1, 2, or 3 from a given number.

Materials

two number cubes, one numbered 1-6 and the other numbered 2-7
Spin Up, Spin Down spinner (see blackline master page 92)
recording paper

Players

one or more

Game

1. Player A rolls the two cubes and adds the two numbers shown, writing a number sentence to record her turn.

2. Player B calls "add" or "subtract" and spins the spinner. If Player B calls "add," Player A adds the number spun (1, 2, or 3) to the sum she found when she completed Step 1. If Player B calls "subtract," Player A subtracts the number spun. Player A writes a second number sentence to record the addition or subtraction problem.

3. Players switch roles and repeat Steps 1 and 2. They continue to take turns until game time is over.

Example

Player A rolls a 3 and a 7. She writes 3 + 7 = 10.
Player B calls "add" and spins a 3.
Player A writes 10 + 3 = 13.

Math News

Directions for Spin Up, Spin Down

Materials   two number cubes, one numbered 1-6 and the other numbered 2-7
Spin Up, Spin Down spinner (attached to this newsletter)
recording paper

Players   one or more

Game
1. Player A rolls the two cubes and adds the two numbers shown, writing a number sentence to record the turn.

2. Player B calls "add" or "subtract" and spins the spinner. If Player B calls "add," Player A adds the number spun (1, 2, or 3) to the sum he or she found when completing Step 1. If Player B calls "subtract," Player A subtracts the number spun. Player A writes a second number sentence to record the addition or subtraction problem.

3. Players switch roles and repeat Steps 1 and 2. Play until one player reaches zero. Then play again!

Example   Player A rolls a 3 and a 7 and writes 3 + 7 = 10.
Player B calls "add" and spins a 3.
Player A writes 10 + 3 = 13.

Skill Update

In class we have been practicing writing addition and subtraction sentences. This game gives your child more practice with these skills!

Challenge

Ask your child to roll both cubes twice and write the four numbers shown. Have your child add the numbers and write an addition sentence to show his or her work. Ask your child to tell what grouping strategies he or she used to add the numbers. For example, to add 3, 4, 5, and 5, you might first add 3 and 4 for a sum of 7, and double 5 to make 10. Then you might add 7 and 10 for a sum of 17.

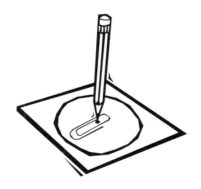

Getting Started with Parents

Dear Parents/Guardians,

Throughout the year your child will be bringing home a
series of arithmetic games for your family to play. The games will be
played with dice (or number cubes), playing cards or spinners. These
three basic, easy to manage materials offer fun ways to add and
subtract, practicing the basic facts. The materials for each game will
be sent home, along with a newsletter that gives directions and
suggestions for making this a successful and enjoyable experience.

Talk to your child about the games. Ask how he or she finds certain
answers. Does he or she have a special way of adding or
subtracting, such as counting up or counting back? Does he or she
break numbers into different parts in order to work with them
more easily? (For example: 9 + 6 is the same as 10 + 5 if they take
1 from the 6 and add it to the 9.) When a child can talk about how
to do a problem, it shows that he or she understands the math and
is not just relying on memorization.

Sometimes it is also good for you, the adult, to talk about how you
work out answers to math problems. It helps if you share how you
learned to add and subtract when you were a child. You can
demonstrate the steps, and if your way is different than your
child's, this is a great chance for him or her to discover
that there are many ways to work through a problem and
still get the correct answer.

Please help your child remember that competition is
secondary. The goal is to have a good time while practicing
the basic facts. Feel free to change the games to make
them more fun and appropriate for your family.

Enjoy!

Helpful Terms

Dear Parents/Guardians,

Before we begin playing math games, here are some common mathematical terms your child will hear and use in our classroom. You'll notice them in the newsletters your child brings home. Please join us in speaking the language of math!

addends: the numbers that are being added together $\underline{7} + \underline{5} = 12$

classroom deck of cards: a regular deck of playing cards with the face cards (kings, queens, jacks and jokers) removed and with aces counting as the number one

difference: the answer in a subtraction problem $6 - 1 = \underline{5}$

doubles: an addition sentence with two addends that are the same $3 + 3 = 6$

fact family: a set of addition and subtraction sentences using the same three numerals in various combinations

$4 + 2 = 6, \quad 2 + 4 = 6$
$6 - 4 = 2, \quad 6 - 2 = 4$

number: the amount of objects in a set ● ● ● ● (four)

number sentence: a written mathematical operation using specific numerals and symbols $2 + 7 = 9$

numeral: the written symbol used to represent a number 8

set: a group of objects represented by a numeral ● ● ● ● ● (5)

sum: the answer in an addition problem $3 + 4 = \underline{7}$

Hundreds Chart

1	2	3	4	5	6	7	8	9	10
11	12	13	14	15	16	17	18	19	20
21	22	23	24	25	26	27	28	29	30
31	32	33	34	35	36	37	38	39	40
41	42	43	44	45	46	47	48	49	50
51	52	53	54	55	56	57	58	59	60
61	62	63	64	65	66	67	68	69	70
71	72	73	74	75	76	77	78	79	80
81	82	83	84	85	86	87	88	89	90
91	92	93	94	95	96	97	98	99	100

Helpful Terms

Dear Parents/Guardians,

Before we begin playing math games, here are some common mathematical terms your child will hear and use in our classroom. You'll notice them in the newsletters your child brings home. Please join us in speaking the language of math!

addends: the numbers that are being added together $\quad\quad\quad$ $\underline{7} + \underline{5} = 15$

classroom deck of cards: a regular deck of playing cards with the face cards (kings, queens, jacks and jokers) removed and with aces counting as the number one

difference: the answer in a subtraction problem $\quad\quad\quad$ $6 - 1 = \underline{5}$

doubles: an addition sentence with two addends that are the same $\quad$ $3 + 3 = 6$

fact family: a set of addition and subtraction sentences that equal the same amount
$$4 + 0 = 4, \quad 0 + 4 = 4$$

number: the amount of objects in a set $\quad\quad\quad$ ● ● ● ● (four)

number sentence: a written mathematical operation using specific numerals and symbols $\quad\quad\quad$ $2 + 7 = 9$

numeral: the written symbol used to represent a number $\quad\quad\quad$ 8

set: a group of objects represented by a numeral $\quad\quad\quad$ ● ● ● ● ● (5)

sum: the answer in an addition problem $\quad\quad\quad$ $3 + 4 = \underline{7}$

Rate This Game

Please take time to fill out this form. Your input helps so much!
There is a space for you and your child to rate the game.
Feel free to add comments. Thanks!

Write the appropriate number next to each question or statement.

KEY: 1 = SOMETIMES   2 = OFTEN   3 = ALWAYS

Title of the Game _____

	Parents	Children
1. Was this game fun?		
2. Was this game too easy?		
3. Was this game too hard?		
4. Would you like to play this game again?		
5. This game was great math practice.		

Comments from parents and children:

Card Game Blacklines

Number/Numeral Cards

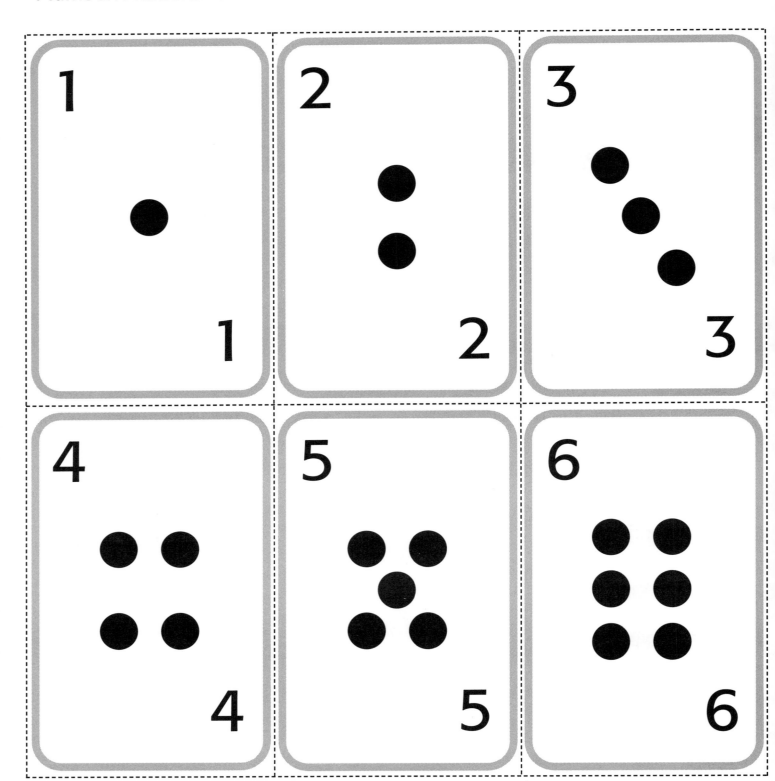

Number/Numeral Cards

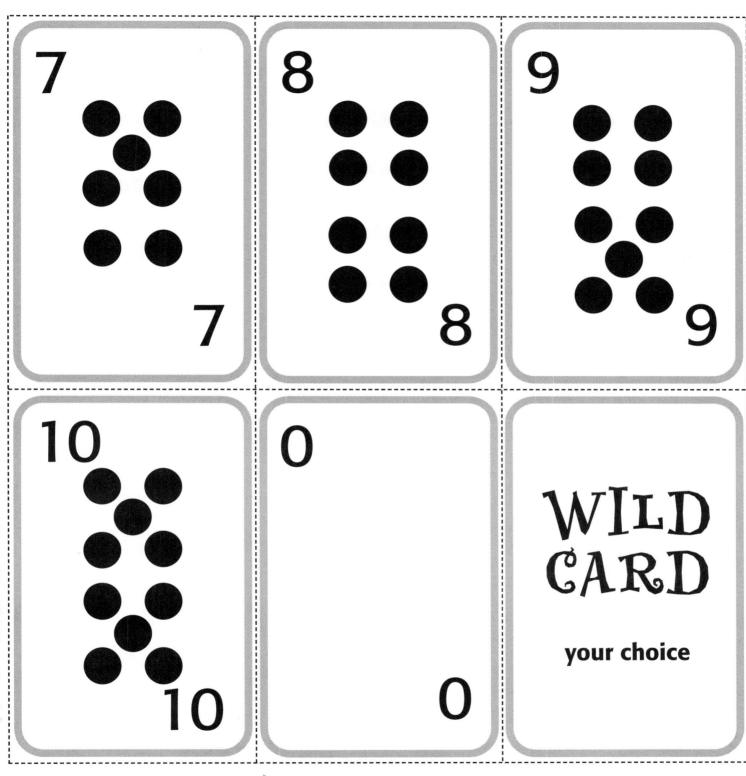

Overhead Cards

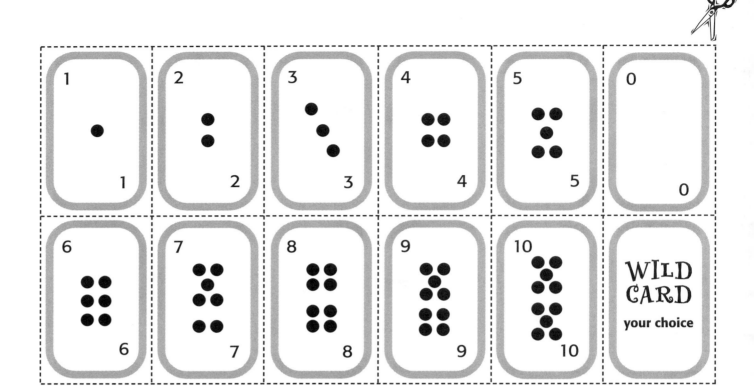

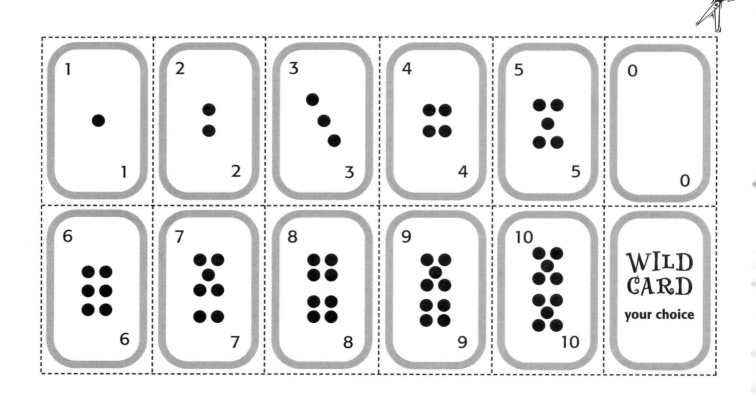

Tens

Ones

Hundreds	Tens	Ones

Dice Blacklines

Graph the Difference

Find the difference between the two numbers. Color the square on the graph which is above your answer.

1	2	3	4	5	6	7	8	9	10	11	12

Doubles Graph

Double the number you have thrown. Color the correct square on the graph.

1	2	3	4	5	6	7	8	9	10	11	12

Penny/Dime Dice

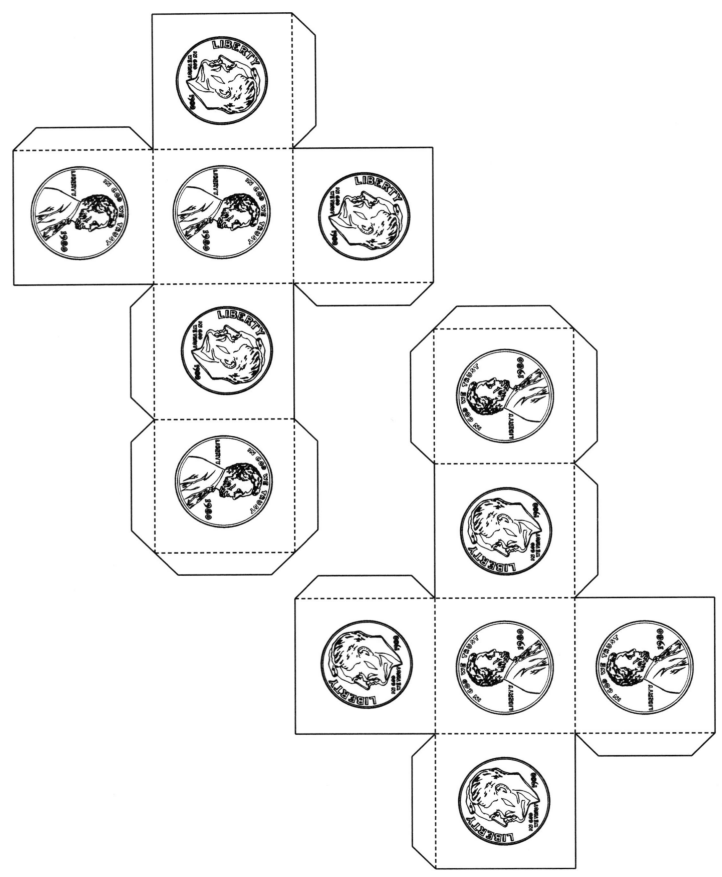

Penny/Dime/Quarter/Nickel Dice

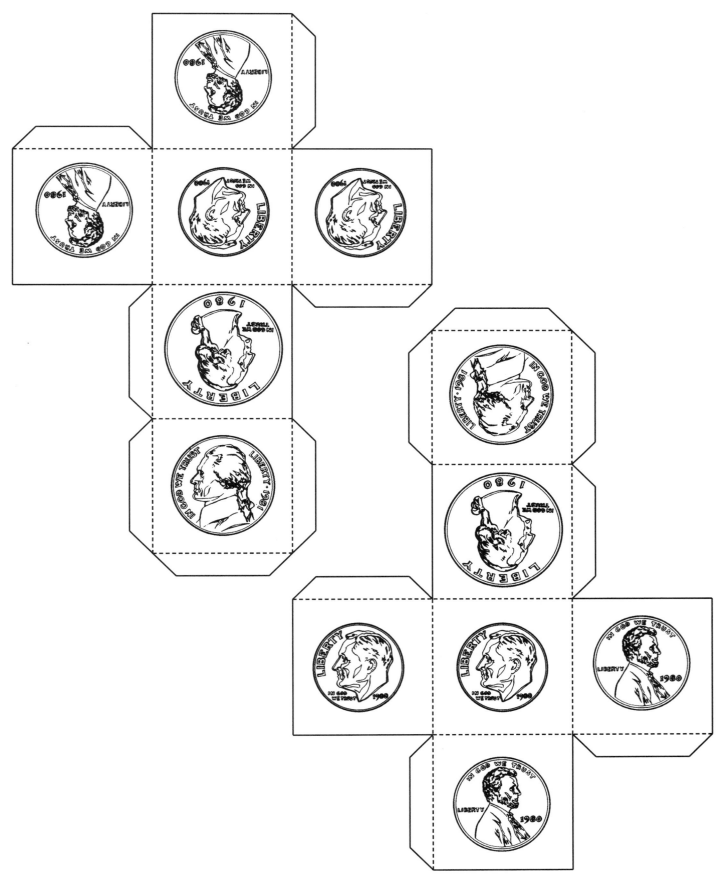

Hundreds Chart

1	2	3	4	5	6	7	8	9	10
11	12	13	14	15	16	17	18	19	20
21	22	23	24	25	26	27	28	29	30
31	32	33	34	35	36	37	38	39	40
41	42	43	44	45	46	47	48	49	50
51	52	53	54	55	56	57	58	59	60
61	62	63	64	65	66	67	68	69	60
71	72	73	74	75	76	77	78	79	80
81	82	83	84	85	86	87	88	89	90
91	92	93	94	95	96	97	98	99	100

Operational Dice

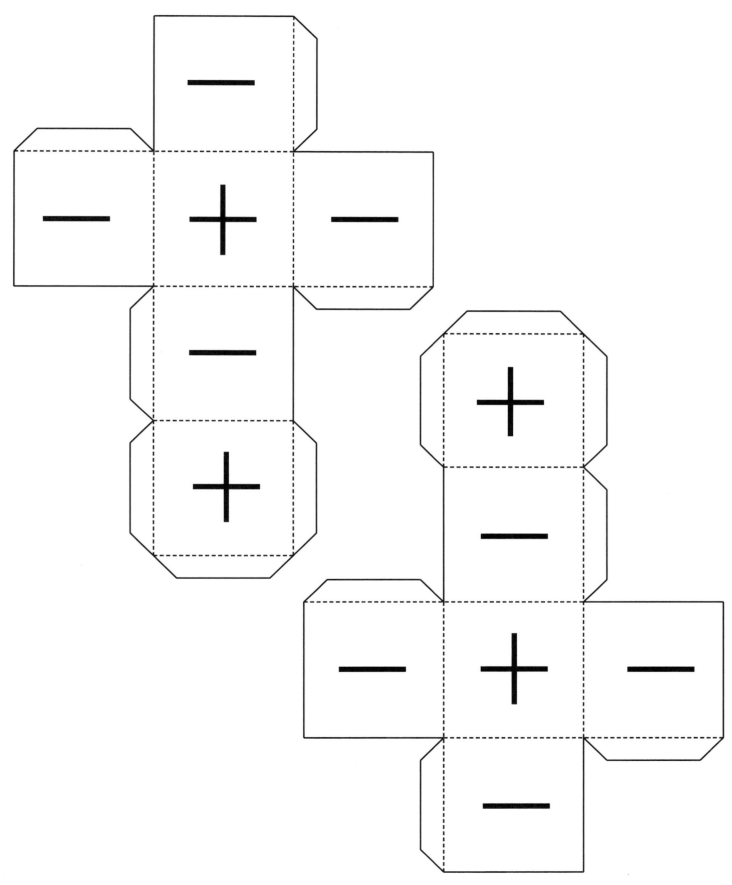

Quick and easy spinner assembly:

Hold the end of a paper clip at the center with a pencil point.
Flick the paper clip as you would for a spinner.

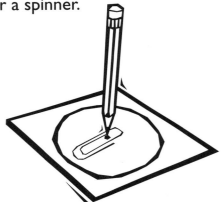

Spinner Blacklines

What's the Difference?

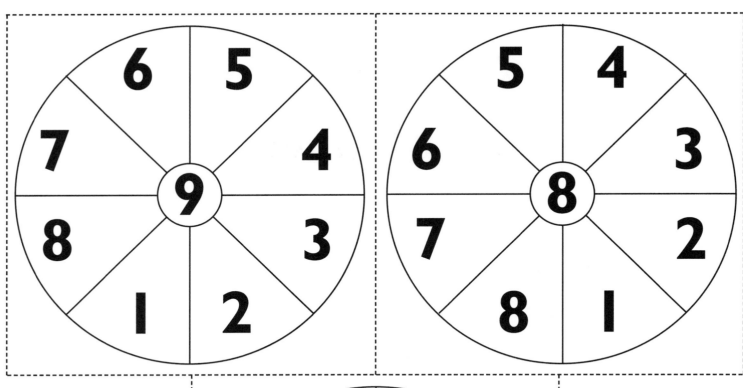

What's the Difference?

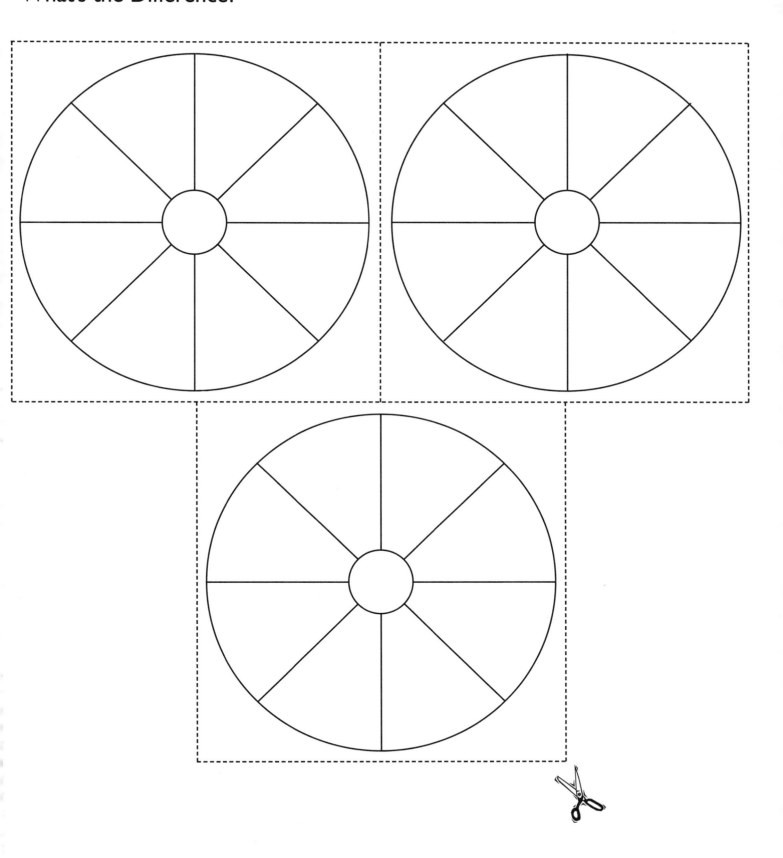

Spin & Spin Again

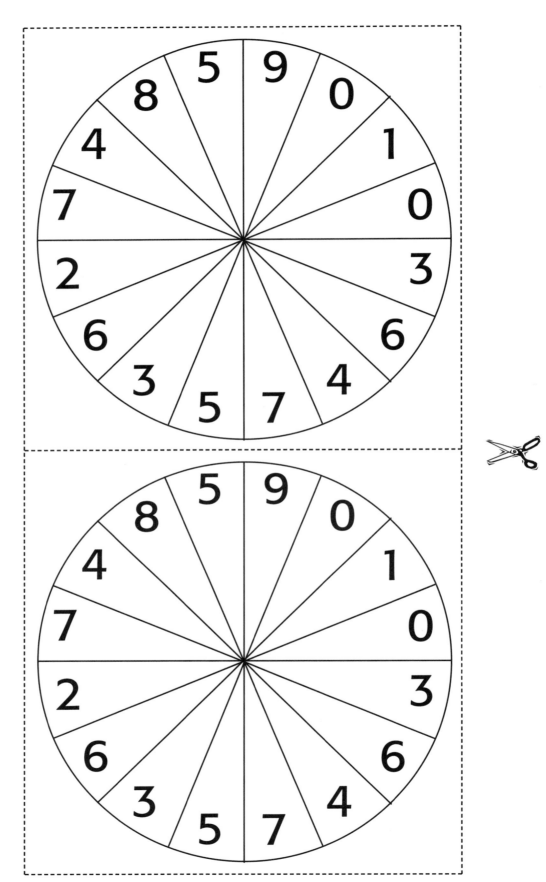

Spin & Spin Again

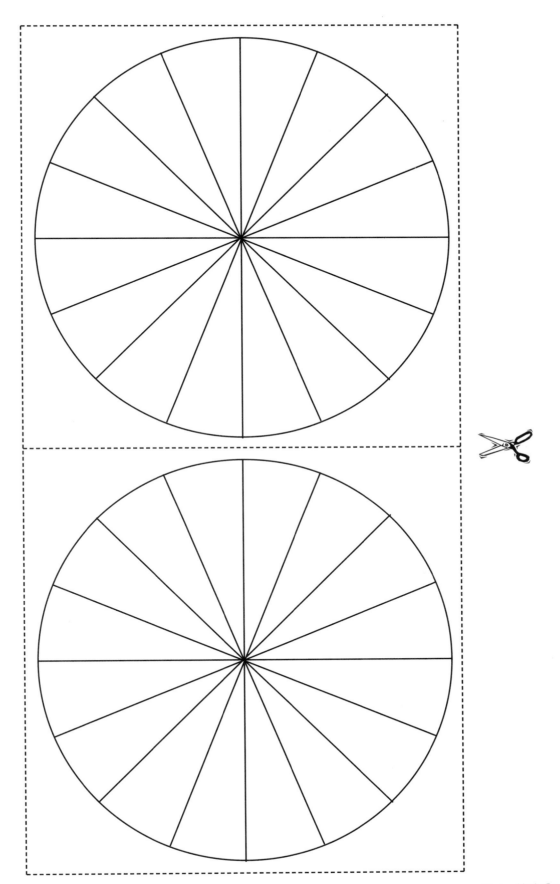

Write 20, Spin Back

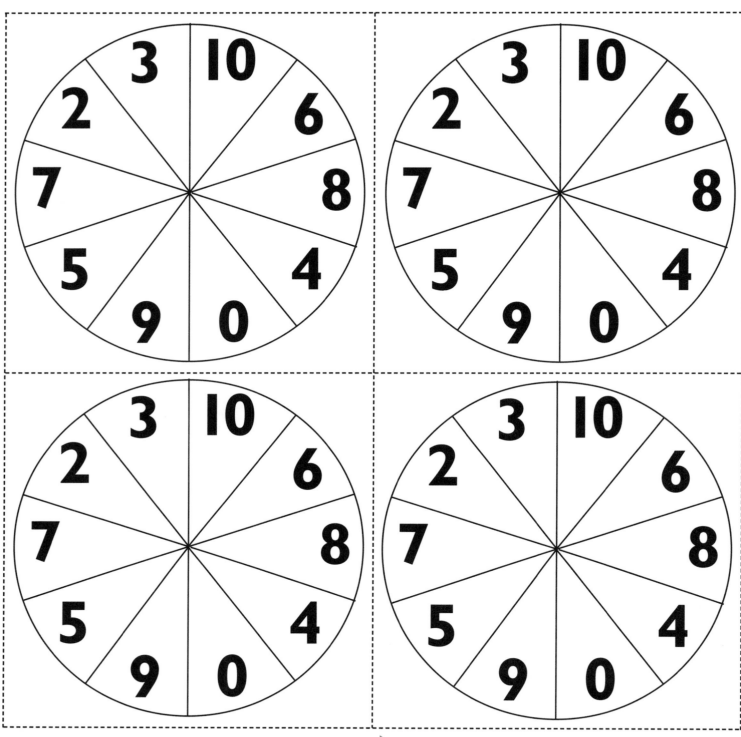

Write 20, Spin Back

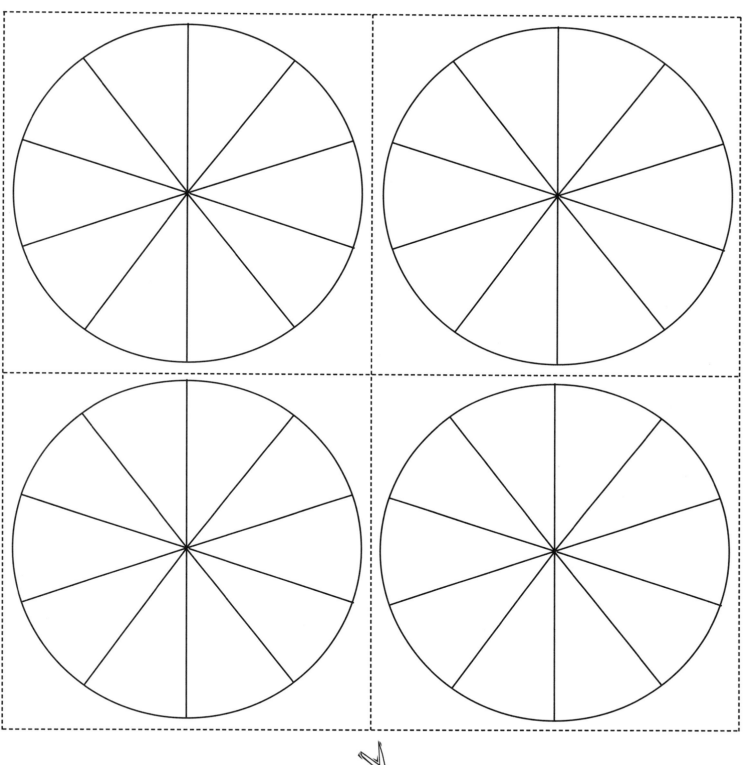

Minus Linus Spinner

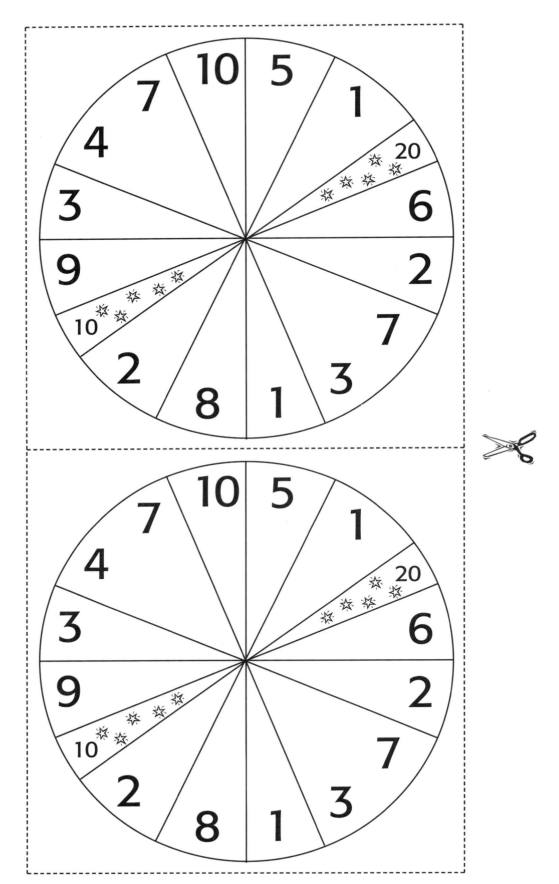

Minus Linus Spinner

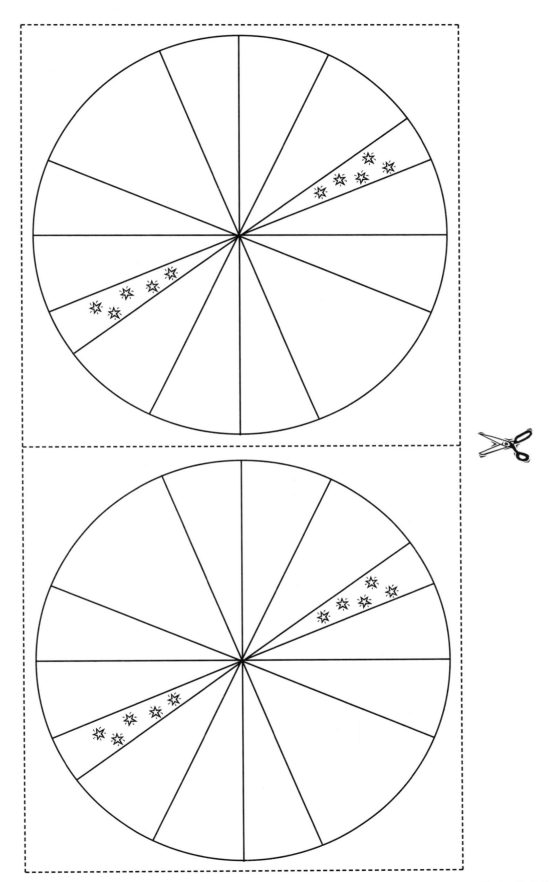

Minus Linus Number Line

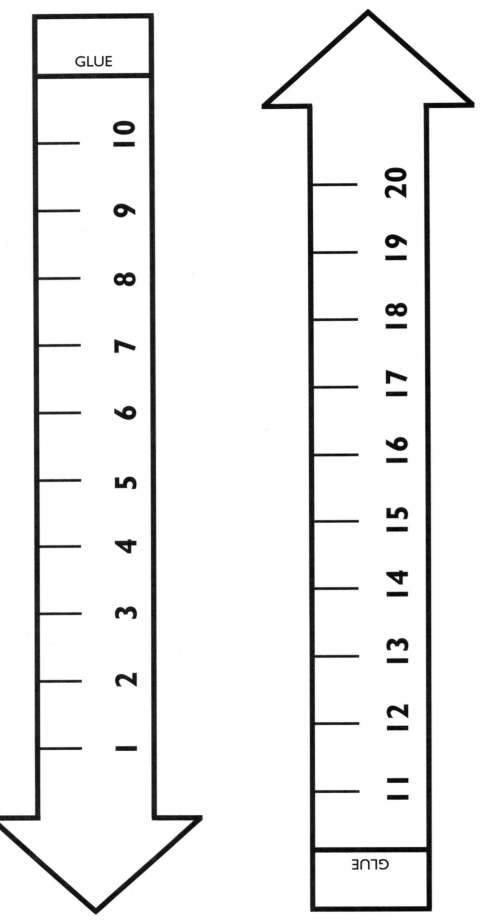

GLUE

10 9 8 7 6 5 4 3 2 1

20 19 18 17 16 15 14 13 12 11

GLUE

Minus Linus Pointer

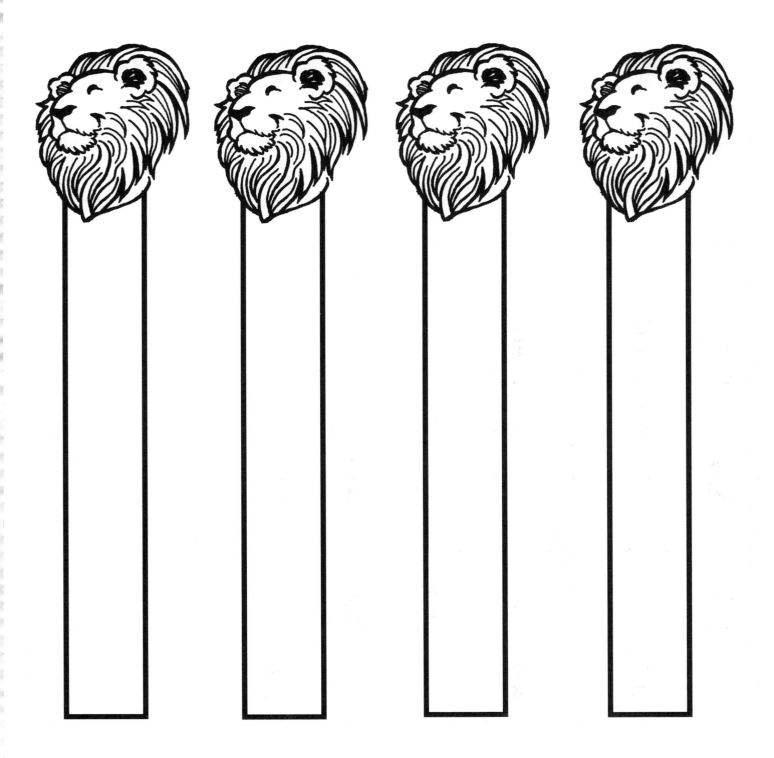

Spin Up, Spin Down

	1	2	
3			3
2			2
	3	1	

	1	2	
3			3
2			2
	3	1	

	1	2	
3			3
2			2
	3	1	

	1	2	
3			3
2			2
	3	1	

Spin Up, Spin Down

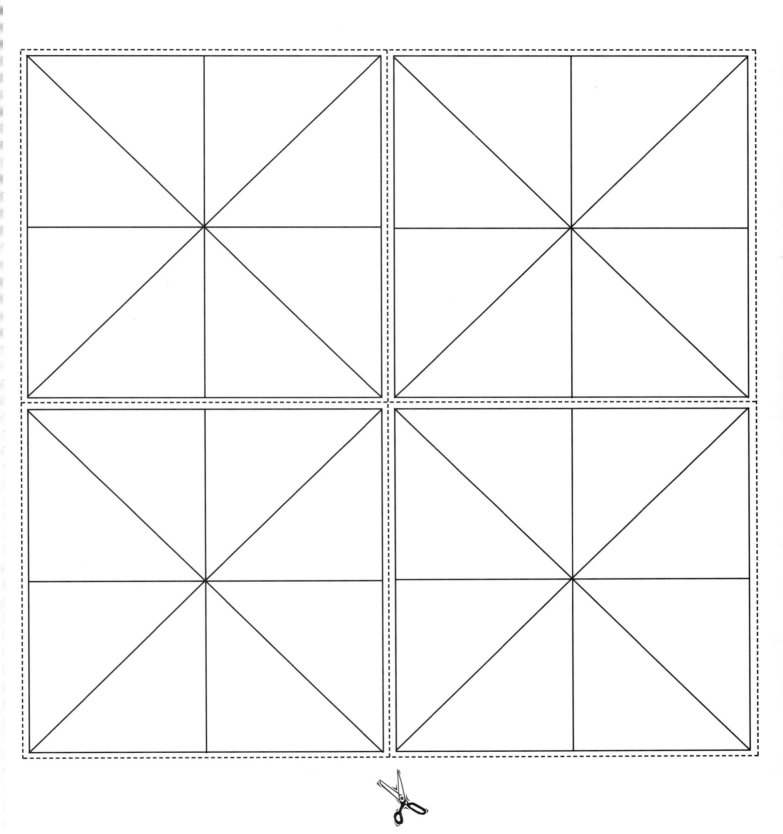